"You have cancer, and I didn't get clean margins."

With those words my life changed –
surprisingly, for the better!

But first, I had to stand up to physicians
who didn't listen to me,
who instead tried to scare me into doing what
they thought I should do.

During a year full of ups and downs
I learned how to explore my options
with curiosity instead of fear,
how to notice the messages my body was sending me,
and how to trust myself, more than the "experts,"
when deciding what was right for me.

I also discovered I can do this in every area of my life.

Francis Andries

About Karin Ireland

Karin Ireland has written 20 books for children and adults and enjoys speaking and leading workshops on subjects that help people create the lives they long to have. Many say her books and workshops served as a wake-up call that led them to take charge of their lives in ways they had not thought possible. She took charge of her own life when she followed her dream to live near the ocean and moved to Newport Beach, California. Years later, she followed her dream to live on a tropical island and moved to Hawaii. After seven years in paradise she trusted her inner voice that it was time to leave and follow another dream to have adventures on the mainland. Turned out she had the best adventure of her life when she moved to Austin, Texas and met the man of her dreams, her soul mate, and married him a year later.

To contact her about workshops or talks or to invite her to participate in other events, please e-mail her at writerki@andries.com. For book or workshop information please visit www.IrelandCommunications.com.

Learning To
Trust Myself

Lessons From Cancer
and Other Life Dilemmas

Karin Ireland

Wise Words Publications
P.O. Box 340337 Austin, TX 78734

This book contains information that is specific to the author and is intended to show possibilities. Readers must make their own decisions about their own medical care.

FIRST EDITION
First Printing, 2004

Library of Congress Catalog Card Number: 2004113121
Library of Congress Cataloging-in-Publication Data
Ireland, Karin
Learning To Trust Myself: Lessons From Cancer and Other Life Dilemmas / Karin Ireland.
p.cm

ISBN 0-9761452-0-0 (pbk)
1. Surviving cancer.   2. Personal empowerment.
3. Self-trust.   4. Intuition.
I. Title.

Quotes from *Don't Take Your Snake For a Stroll*, Harcourt 2003

Printed by Litho Press, San Antonio, Texas

Dedication

This book is dedicated to women everywhere who are trying to find their own voice – whether it's at home, at work, or in the doctor's office. It's dedicated to women who hear their own voice but aren't sure they have the right to listen – you do! You must! And it's dedicated to everyone who is trying to be who they really are; loving, kind and courageous.

This book is dedicated to Tricia Ireland Stirling, as always, for everything.

And especially to Francis Andries, my soul mate, who encouraged me to write this and who encourages me to be who and what I want to be.

Acknowledgments

So many people reached out, eager to help me find the path I was searching for. There aren't enough words to thank you. Without you, I might have let myself be pushed into risky treatment I didn't want. Also possible: The cure would have killed more than the cancer and I wouldn't have survived. Please know that you just may have saved my life.

Thank you Burton Goldberg, Caroline Myss and Bernie Siegel M.D. Your books and tapes gave me courage and direction and helped me be strong enough to take charge of my life. Thank you Sid for being there, and Kathy for helping me find the path; thank you Julie Castiglia, my agent and friend for years and years, and thank you, Dad, for making the alternative possible.

Mahalo Nui Loa Winona, Gladys, Robert, Rita and all the rest of the Pohulani lunch bunch for being my ohana.

Thank you Sherry Vinson, for your wise insights, psychic and otherwise, and thank you Theresa Castro for graciously sharing your information and ideas. Thank you John Vinson and Violet Donoghue for your patient editing and wise insights. Thank you Susan Price for editing and taking this from manuscript to book format.

Thank you Tricia Ireland Stirling. For everything, as always. Thank you Shane, Tyler and Irie for being wonderful. I love you.

And a huge, huge thank you to Francis Andries. I could write a book about how much you mean to me.

The main thing
Is to keep the main thing
The main thing.

– Alan Cohen

After a century of pill-and-scalpel medicine,
we've discovered that fighting disease
and restoring health
are not the same.
– *Newsweek*

First, do no harm.
– Attributed to the Hippocratic Oath

Foreword

Karin Ireland is funny, spiritual and – as these engaging pages reveal – self-motivated and driven. Diagnosed with a 6 cm tumor identified as invasive lobular carcinoma, she wanted *both* conventional *and* alternative treatment but notes the dearth of oncologists willing to adjust their view to her vision. Her story chronicles her search for *integrative* cancer care in her fight for life, and of her awareness that for a doctor to help you he must first believe that he can.

Plights like Karin's ignited my own fire 25 years ago. As a medical student jarred by limitations in patient care, I sought to provide kinder, gentler, and incrementally advanced therapies. I recognized early on that combining treatment strategies could often have a synergistic and thus more effective clinical result.

It was 1980 and it led me and my wife to develop and implement a comprehensive program of integrative cancer care – specifically the one that was highlighted and described as archetypically "the model program" in *"Unconventional Cancer Treatments,"* a 1990 published document prepared by the U.S. Office of Technology Assessment for the Congress of the United States (essentially a study report assessing and evaluating various adjunctive cancer therapies being utilized by the American population).

Since the primary goal for every cancer patient is to reduce the tumor burden while fortifying the body, I believed blending conventional and alternative treatment into an integrative program would be the *consummate* way to keep cancer patients alive and well. Our clinical work confirms this, including the fact that it is possible to soften even the harsher therapies. We began providing less toxic, effective chemotherapy (when needed) with fractionated dosing and circadian timed infusions. Then, as Karin concludes, we felt everyone with cancer deserves prescriptive nutrition with herbal and nutrient supplementation, therapeutic exercise, acupuncture, and mind-spirit techniques as part of their care. Also, by performing advanced biochemical lab testing and tumor tissue analysis to determine molecular targets, it is possible to develop a comprehensive, disease-specific and individualized treatment plan.

Even with a physician filled with hope, guidance and a recovery plan in mind, patients still must choose their own course. Karin did exactly that. Along with a growing army of informed patients, she is navigating her own cancer battle and now celebrates many years being cancer-free.

Her book offers hope and insight as she tells of doing it *her* way and outlines how she got to have her cake and eat it too – vegan and sugar-free, of course!

Keith I. Block, M.D.
Medical & Scientific Director of the Block Center for Integrative Cancer Care and the Institute for Cancer Research & Education
Editor-in-Chief, *Integrative Cancer Therapies,* Sage Science Press
Clinical Assistant Professor, University of Illinois College of Medicine
Adjunct Assistant Professor of Pharmacognosy, College of Pharmacy, University of Illinois
Medical Consultant on Nutritional-Oncology Research for the Office of Technology Assessment for the Congress of the United States.

Why I Wrote This Book

On October 17, 1997, my surgeon told me she'd removed a 6-7 centimeter invasive lobular carcinoma from my right breast. She said she was sorry, she hadn't gotten clean margins so I'd need to have a mastectomy, then probably chemotherapy and radiation.

I sobbed while she recited statistics on how long I might be expected to live if I followed my doctors' recommendations. They weren't very comforting. Everyone I'd known who had had cancer had died, so I believed I would, too.

But I've found that when I'm on the wrong path, something – my spirit? God? the Universe? – nudges me in another direction. After I recovered some from the shock, I remembered that I'd always been interested in alternative medicine and I started looking for a doctor who could suggest less drastic therapies to help me be well.

I also began to notice that my body was talking to me, sending messages of its own. I felt heavy with dread and fear and hopelessness when my doctors talked to me about the treatment they insisted I needed to have but I felt light and powerful and optimistic when I thought about finding a way to get well that wouldn't make me sicker first.

In my search I discovered there is valid research to prove that dozens of alternative therapies can cure cancer and there are dozens of highly respected medical and naturopathic doctors in the United States who are quietly saving lives by the thousands using these therapies. Many have patients who have survived more than a decade (and are still living) after being told by traditional doctors that they would die within weeks.

Unfortunately, these open-minded physicians are still a small minority and I had a difficult time finding one who practiced in Hawaii.

Here's a scary fact: Statistics from the National Cancer Institute show that with all the money and technology traditional medicine is using to battle the disease, the death rate between 1950 and 1999 actually rose 3.8 percent.

Why? I believe a good amount of the increase can be blamed on changes in our society's lifestyle that leave us more vulnerable – diet, stress, lack of meaningful exercise – but some of the increase can be blamed on the toxic methods used to try to cure cancer. Traditional methods are so damaging to the body that some people, like my mother, are cured of cancer but become too weak to survive the cure.

I think we have to accept that some people will die of cancer no matter what treatment they choose. What I'm not willing to accept is the double standard: If someone dies after traditional treatment, people applaud a valiant fight and blame the cancer. But if someone uses alternative medicine and dies (often after traditional doctors have given up), it's the treatment that gets the blame. That thinking needs to change.

Soon after my diagnosis I realized that while my choice of medical care was important to my survival, so were my choices about how I lived my life. I don't believe that cancer just happens, I believe that basically our bodies know how to be healthy and when they aren't it's because they aren't getting everything they need.

I'd let mine become a good host to cancer. I'd known my diet wasn't good and I'd promised to lay off the desserts and junk food. But I was always going to do it "tomorrow." I'd known about the benefits of exercise and I'd joined a gym and even gone for awhile, then I'd come up with excuses to miss and eventually I quit. I seemed to attract high-stress jobs and then stay in them, pushing myself almost to the point of collapse. I kept making excuses about why I couldn't/shouldn't quit. Instead of relaxing in my time off, I'd take on more projects than I could possibly complete but I'd push myself to complete them anyway.

I realized that if I didn't make some significant changes, my body would remain a good host to cancer. It isn't easy to change, but it's possible.

I sincerely hope you'll never hear a cancer or other life-threatening diagnosis for yourself or a loved one but if you do, I hope my story will help.

Some names have been changed.

Looking Back a Little

When I think of myself as a child there are two words that come to mind: *compliant* and *frustrated*. I did pretty much what the people in authority told me to do, but I was frustrated because half the time it didn't make sense.

For example, I didn't understand why I had to put on a sweater when my dad got cold or why, whenever my parents and I disagreed, *I* was always the one who was wrong. I didn't understand why everything I said seemed to hurt my mother's feelings, cause her to go to her room and cry until I apologized or why my dad always took her side. When there were conflicts I'd argue some, try to explain, try to get them to understand me, but eventually I'd give up.

I was compliant and frustrated at school, too. I went to class every day and tried to pay attention, but most of the subjects bored me and I had a hard time re-membering facts and names and dates so I didn't do very well.

I loved gym, though, and did well except for one semester in the 10th grade. I was thrilled when my boyfriend gave me his ring to wear on a chain around my neck and I wore it proudly to school. My gym teacher gave me a demerit, though, and told me not to wear it to class because it could hurt someone. I figured if I wore the ring tucked inside my (laundered and ironed every Monday) cotton gym shirt it would be out of the way and everyone would be safe.

She never mentioned the ring again and I thought that I'd been a good problem solver. But I guess she didn't want me to think; she just wanted me to do what she told me to do because she gave me an F on my report card. "What will people *think* of me?" cried my mother. No one at school even knew her so I didn't understand why she was so upset. But she told my dad and I was punished and I didn't wear the ring to class again.

I was 19, hearing my dad angry with my brother, again, when I decided to quit school and move out. I felt like I would explode if I had to keep hearing my dad constantly criticizing my brother without being able to do anything about it. I'd tried to get my mother to make my dad understand how unfair he was and I think she tried. John was a sweet 9-year-old kid, a good kid most parents would be proud to claim but our dad never seemed to see it that way.

I didn't tell my parents I planned to move until after I'd gotten a job at a bank and rented a tiny apartment with a tiny living room, kitchen and bath.

It wasn't long before I discovered there was a whole world full of people who wanted to tell me what to do. Of course I brought my old habits to my new work and personal relationships. I'd stand up for myself to a point, try to get them to understand, and then I'd give in. Sometimes I gave in because I felt powerless against their power and sometimes I gave in because I questioned whether I deserved to have or say or do what I wanted to. At home I'd never won an argument, so I assumed I wouldn't win any in the outside world, either.

Mostly, I blended in with all the other 20-something women I knew but every once in a while I'd find myself interested in something that set me apart. In the late '60s I raised eyebrows at work by taking judo and then karate at a time when it wasn't popular for females to be physically aggressive. I enjoyed the sport but having a green belt also made me feel special. In my daydreams I imagined myself helping Emma Peal on *The Avengers*. She was my role model, she was strong, confident, intelligent, everything I wasn't but wished I were.

I read books about Edgar Cayce before Shirley MacLaine went out on a limb introducing metaphysics to the general population and I decided reincarnation made sense at a time when most people thought that meant I believed I might come back as a cow.

Years later, many workshops and books and tapes later, I came to believe that we create our experiences by the things we think and talk about and I tried to be positive. Cancer was the new dreaded disease and since I definitely didn't want to have it, I used to tell myself I never would and I was positive I wouldn't. I told myself I wasn't the type (which I had read was angry), and I knew that if I *truly believed* it, I'd live a cancer-free life.

The notion that I could will myself to avoid cancer didn't seem unreasonable because I do have an interesting history of being able to affect my health with my stubbornness. When I was about 11, my mother took me to the doctor with yet another sty – this time on the bottom lid of my right eye. I sat on the edge of his examining table and held my breath while he sliced it open. Then he turned to my mother and said that if I got one more sty, she should have my eyes examined for glasses.

Kids' glasses weren't cute in those days and I felt I already stood out – too shy, too tall, too skinny. Dread tightened my chest. I'd be teased even more…. I never had another sty. Not one.

In my early 20s, I'd often wake up in the morning with a cyst filled with clear fluid on one side of my mouth in the bottom corner under my tongue. Eventually I went to the doctor to ask what to do. He said the next time I had one I should come in right away and he'd do surgery to remove it. I remember feeling woozy as he explained how he'd put a tube down my throat to knock me out, how he'd carefully cut the tissue away and stitch up the incision and...I never had another cyst.

In my late 20s I had a terrible case of flu, so bad I couldn't get off the couch for five days. I determined I'd never have the flu again and would confidently tell people each season that I never got the flu...and for more than 30 years, I didn't.

And there was the time when I started bleeding and knew from past experience that the doctor would recommend a D&C. *If I create my experiences,* I asked myself, *why am I creating this? What would the payoff be for another D&C?*

Immediately I realized that when I'd had the first D&C my (now ex) husband had been full of concern. Was I unconsciously looking for a way to pull him close again? *Not this way,* I decided, and the bleeding stopped.

* * *

I'd been happily married for several years and then unhappily for several when I first started hearing the whispers of my inner voice. *No,* I told it, *I can't get a divorce.* Our daughter was just two, and Tricia and her dad had a great relationship. What right did I have to tear them apart just because I was miserable?

But the thing about my inner voice is that it's *very* patient and *very* persistent. It kept talking and one morning five years later I woke up and knew, between one heartbeat and the next, that I couldn't stay married any longer. I didn't just know it intellectually, I *felt* the knowing in my body.

I was terrified, I felt guilty and sad, but I also felt a calmness and resolve in my solar plexus that separating and eventually divorcing was the right thing to do. And it turned out it was. He and I stayed in the same neighborhood as co-parents and my ex and our daughter developed an even closer relationship.

Five years later Tricia and I spent a vacation day in Newport Beach in Southern California. The sun was warm, the sky was blue with puffy white clouds – the day was perfect. We walked along the beach then decided it would be fun to rent bicycles and take them on the ferry to Balboa Island.

Balboa Island was different, it *felt* different, than anyplace we'd ever been and we liked the feeling a lot. It was a cozy place where neighbors talked, where people greeted you from their porches, where strangers got into conversations at street corners. We rode slowly past houses next to mansions next to small cottages, past wood and brick and stucco, each home so different but each fitting in perfectly.

The yards had their own personalities, too. Some had fences, low ones with gates that seemed to invite you in rather than keep you out; some had grass, some were wild with flowers and a few were as empty as the sand near the ocean. We dodged walkers, runners and skaters on the walkway that circled the island and felt more at home than we did in our own neighborhood.

We pedaled to the village, just three blocks long but crowded with clothing boutiques and small restaurants and small shops that tempted us with exotic coffees, fresh-baked muffins, homemade ice cream or frozen bananas dipped in chocolate and nuts. A winding brick path led to a little bookstore owned by two sisters. People here were happy. *We* were happy here, too.

A chill was in the ocean breeze by the time we ferried back over the bay. We surrendered our bikes, found our car and headed home.

"Can't we move here, Mom?" Tricia asked. I wished with all my heart that we could but told her no, I couldn't afford it. Still, we fantasized about living there for days before closing it up in our collection of impossible dreams.

But from time to time I remembered the way the sun had felt on my skin, the way *I* had felt in Balboa. My inner voice whispered about adventure, trading the safe but boring known for the adventures of a new community. It whispered about seeing the sparkling blue water every day, of feeling the way I feel only when I'm near the ocean. My logical mind always said no, even if I found a beach town I could afford, I couldn't separate Tricia and her dad by a two-hour drive. Even if I knew we'd both be happy there.

Later that year I started noticing synergy – an event or series of events that are connected to a question or something I need to know. A friend opened a shop in a beach town and sometimes I'd go there to visit her. I loved driving streets where the ocean would unexpectedly appear in the distance. Beach towns felt different, glimpses of ocean were a treat I wished I could have more of.

I'd love to live at the beach, I told myself and I told friends at work, too. But it was a daydream, nothing I expected to do. Then within one 48-hour period three people told me the same thing: Tricia and her dad would be fine if we moved but I wouldn't be unless I did what I needed to do for *me*. That was a new thought, doing something to be good to myself.

A few months later, a year after Tricia and I spent

that day at Balboa, I decided to go away for the weekend, just by myself. I pushed past my logical mind, which said spending money on an outing just for me was wasteful, and I booked a hotel room for one in Newport Beach, just a few miles from Balboa. I walked the beach, picked up shells, had a hamburger at the end of the pier. The next morning I drove south to Laguna Beach and treated myself to a beachfront breakfast and lingered over coffee. I looked past the sandy beach to the ocean and I knew, between one heartbeat and the next, mind and body, that if I could find a place I could afford I would move.

I bought a paper and discovered that there actually *were* condos in beach towns that fit my budget. Not on Balboa Island, not in Laguna, but in Newport Beach and I liked Newport Beach just fine. I left the restaurant and drove west on Pacific Coast Highway and in Corona Del Mar I spotted a realty office.

"Newport Beach? You want Valerie," said the realtor. "I'll call and tell her you're coming." How easy was this?

Valerie drove me around to look at a few characterless houses and then down a street and around a curve to sprawling tree-filled grassy hills with two-story blue condos that overlooked a wilderness area. It felt perfect. I loved it and I knew Tricia would, too. There was nothing for sale there but the realtor promised to find a seller; I bought tourist post cards for my bulletin board at work and visualized my new home.

Tricia and I had a wonderful time living in Newport Beach but eight years later she was in college in northern California, planning to stay north of San Francisco after graduation, and my inner voice started calling me from Hawaii. I'd been there twice – once married and once single – and I hadn't wanted to leave. I remembered gentle breezes, friendly people, spectacular sunsets, water so clear you could see right through it. Over the years I'd asked friends dozens of times, "What would it take for you to drive to the airport right now and buy a ticket to Hawaii? What would it take for you to live there forever?" Each time I was really asking myself.

One of the goals I always wrote in my goal journals was to live on a tropical island for six months with the option of staying. Hawaii was paradise, and I told myself I'd move there in a minute, if only I could ... but I had a long list of reasons I couldn't.

Then one afternoon, while I was watching the sunset on the beach at 34th Street, the voice stopped asking. "More sunsets, in Hawaii," it said, as clearly as if someone were standing next to me and in that very instant I felt calm, mind and body, and knew I was moving.

I hated the idea of being so far from my daughter but I'd taught her to follow her dreams and now she encouraged me to follow mine. I reshaped my budget to save money and for the next couple of weeks I got synergistic messages confirming that I really was supposed to move: I ran into an old friend who had just returned from studying Huna…in Honolulu. I chatted with a stranger on Balboa Island who started telling me about the years she'd lived in Hawaii. The health food store I'd shopped in almost daily for nearly eight years piped out, for the first time, *Hawaiian* music….

I told my Huna friend I planned to go there to find a job and a place to live before actually moving there and he asked, why? Why not just move there and then find a job? I told him I wasn't that brave.

Eventually my logical self pointed out to my not-so-brave self that it would cost me nearly $2,000 to go and come back, and accumulating an extra $2,000 would add months to my hoped-for departure date. I knew I was moving to Hawaii whether I found a job right away or not, so why not just go? My body felt calm and my mind said, okay.

I reserved a room at the Honolulu Wilder Street Y but then a friend gave me the number of a friend who (serendipitously) had a friend with a vacant room in her house to rent. I called, we talked and I sent her a check.

The first week of January, 1994, I booked a one-way flight, leased out my Newport Beach condo, packed 17 boxes with essentials and called Salvation Army to haul away five rooms of furniture.

Early Valentine's Day morning, in the middle of a terrific thunderstorm, I locked the door of my empty condo and climbed into an airport van – as confident as if I were going to the corner market for a carton of milk.

Several hours later my plane banked over Pearl Harbor and I looked down at brilliant blue water dotted with white sails; a cluster of small boxes that was downtown Honolulu; to the left the lush green slope of Tantalus; and hovering grayish-white clouds that shaded and sometimes sprinkled the island. I thanked God, the Universe, my higher power and the land that is Hawaii; I knew I had come home.

* * *

Oahu is beautiful, the people are the friendliest in the world, and I was very happy. But even in paradise scary things happen. I'd lived there for three years when the scariest thing of my whole life happened to me.

Since I'd decided I was never going to have cancer, I was lax about getting mammograms. I believed that you find what you're looking for so I never really did self-exams, either.

I was in the shower one morning when I felt a lump the size of a small candy bar on the outer side of my right breast. I was concerned, but not afraid. My mother had had cancer and six months later she'd died. My dad's new wife's former husband had had cancer and he'd died. No one I'd ever known had survived cancer so I knew for sure that my lump wasn't cancer.

Besides, I'd read that cancer feels like a small pea, or a marble if it's larger, but round, not rectangular like a Junior Snickers. I decided what I'd found was just a lot of fibrous tissue but I did make an appointment for my annual exam, and planned to go for a mammogram since I hadn't had one in 10 years. Looking back, it's amazing how effortlessly I lived in denial.

It's also amazing, looking back, how many of my adult experiences replicated those of my childhood, each giving me another opportunity to take charge in a positive way, to think and behave differently. But it took having cancer for me to do it.

When I started writing this book I thought it would be about having cancer and searching for ways to be well without having to be sicker first. But about half way through the first draft I realized that it's about much more – cancer was just the name of the latest dilemma in my life, the latest opportunity for me to learn something I've needed to learn all my life. This book is also about learning to trust myself.

Notes From My Journal

Late August, 1997

Thursday. I have new insurance this year so I had to go to a new OB/GYN for my annual check-up. I was only a little bit apprehensive to see what she'd say about the lump in my breast. The nurse showed me to a room and handed me a strip of paper about half the length of the shapeless things they used to call a gown. I undressed and stuck my arms through the holes, then twisted the front into a knot.

A few minutes later there was a knock and a Chinese woman in her late 30s introduced herself as Dr. Lee. She seemed nice, and efficient. We chatted while she did the pap smear then palpated both breasts. She said I should get a mammogram, handed me an authorization slip and left without saying a word about the lump. That's good, though, isn't it? If she'd have been worried she'd have said something. I haven't had a mammogram in 10 years, though, so I'll definitely have one done.

* * *

Early September, 1997

Tuesday. I checked in for my mammogram and a few minutes later a technician led me to a closet-size room and gave me a gown to put on. I pulled it tight around me then went to wait in a drafty hallway with other patients who were waiting for X-rays. I sneaked a look: Every one of us pretended not to notice that we were basically undressed and surrounded by strangers. Interesting.

Every mammogram I promise myself that I won't grumble, but I'm convinced that if the men who design these machines were having these tests they'd have built them so a person wouldn't have to push their chest forward while pulling their chin back, torque one shoulder right while twisting the other shoulder left and, at the same time, have a sensitive piece of their body mashed flat between two hard, cold plastic plates.

Afterwards I went back to the hall to wait for the technician to say I could leave. But when she came back she said the doctor wanted a magnified picture of my right breast. Would I please follow her?

I wanted to say, *I know there's a lump there, but it's okay.* If it was anything to worry about Dr. Lee would have said something, right?

Afterward I went back to my same seat in the hall and a few minutes later the technician came back to say the doctor wants to see my last X-rays, compare them to these, and would I please have them sent to him? I'm worried a little but I know it's not cancer so I make myself think about other things.

* * *

Late September, 1997

Tuesday. The lab called to say my X-rays from California have arrived and the doctor wants to do another X-ray for comparison and could I please come in ASAP? I don't like the sound of that. I reminded myself, *I know there's a lump there and I know it's not cancer.* I'm not a cancer person. I know that, but I'm worried some.

* * *

Friday. I did the follow-up mammogram today, and now I wait.

* * *

Tuesday. I came home and there was a message on my machine from Dr. Lee. "I need to talk to you about your X-rays. Could you please call me right away?" My insides felt like they caved in a little but I reminded myself it's not cancer. I made an appointment for tomorrow and am trying to push it out of my mind. Some of the time I actually can – all I have to do is think about my job.

I'm making no money, working as hard as I can so I can afford to quit. The commission structure guarantees that the company won't have to pay the sales staff more than the barest minimum and our sales manager is the worst boss in town, maybe on the planet. Gunther is smarmy sweet when things are going well for him, ugly angry when they aren't.

At work my stomach is constantly in knots and my shoulders are always tight.

* * *

October, 1997

Wednesday. I went to see Dr. Lee and she showed me the X-rays from California (clear) and then the ones taken last month. She pointed to an area of gray and inside that a spot that was dark. She said the report called that area "quite suspicious" and said "removal is strongly recommended."

I felt a jolt of fear when she said that but I'm pushing it down pretty well. Doctors have to err on the side of caution, don't they? I've always known I'll never have cancer but I do know that whatever the lump is, it doesn't belong there, and I should have it removed.

She gave me a surgeon's name and told me to make an appointment to see her right away. She didn't mention whether she'd felt the lump during the exam and I didn't ask. It'd sound like a criticism and what's the point?

Later. I need to focus on the positive things about my job. I get paid to drive around Oahu. I get to meet people. It could be an okay place to work except for Gunther. His Monday morning rah rah staff meetings make me crazy but he insists on them, even though Steve and I are the only two sales reps left.

Gunther says his mentors tell him all sales people have Monday morning meetings so we have to, too. He wants us to be cheery and motivated and he gets sarcastic because we aren't. We're working too hard for what little money we make and these meetings don't do a thing to help and when we tell him what would help he promises to make changes but he never does. I tell myself that I'm evolved enough to just show up and not let him upset me but every single Monday morning I kick myself for not having realized that I'm not and I can't.

His management style drove off all eight of the sales reps he hired plus the two who were here before he took the job. Some quit the day they were hired (I'd considered that myself), some stayed a week or two. Only a couple stayed more than a month. Steve has been there the longest (after me) and he's talking about leaving. I beg him pleeeze, don't quit and leave me here all alone.

I wish I could quit but I can't and I really believe that if I can just hang on till Christmas I'll make some money and then I can afford to quit. Oh, I was trying to be positive....

* * *

Thursday. Today I went to visit the surgeon. It was nice to just sit for a few minutes in Dr. Nagao's office. Compared to the place I work, hers is a haven of calm. Calm music. Calm colors. Calm magazines (current ones!) lying calmly on a table by the couch. I tried to be calm.

She came to the waiting room to get me, wearing a trendy beige suit that made her look more like a model in *Vogue* than a surgeon. She has that Japanese swingy jet-black hair I've always lusted after.

She introduced herself, offered me a seat in her *Vogue*-like office and clipped my X-rays to the light box on the wall. She pointed to the gray area and said, "There's a 2.5 x 1.5 cm speculated mass in the outer quadrant of the right breast at approximately the 9:00 o'clock to 9:30 location with architectural distortion." Then, in layman's terms, "The mass is cancer."

Outwardly, I didn't move but I felt my insides cave in again. My thoughts raced in a dozen directions at once. I told myself, she *can't* be right. I've *always* known I wouldn't have cancer. I noticed she was talking again, telling me that studies show that a lumpectomy is as effective as a mastectomy if the cancer is all in one place. Cancer!

She said she'd request a procedure called needle localization, which would be done at the hospital just before the surgery. Step one, a doctor would insert a large needle (with a smaller fish-hook needle inside) into my breast, using the most suspicious part of the lump as the target. When he thought the needle was close to the target, he'd do a mammogram with the needle still in my breast. If his aim was off, he'd keep probing and X-raying until he got the tip of the needle resting at the spot she thinks is cancer. Once the doctor was satisfied, he'd leave the needle in my breast as a guide for her during surgery.

I felt faint. I'm not good with pain and this sounds like torture to me. I wanted to say, *are you crazy? The lump is so large a blind surgeon wouldn't be able to miss it!*

I asked her about other options and she said there aren't any. She was calm, precise, and inflexible, and it made me uncomfortable.

The words "second surgical opinion" sounded really good and I told her I need time to think about what I'm going to do. I went to the car and sat in the parking lot till I could stop shaking.

I drove back to work but it was hard to get her voice out of my head. Even with Gunther yammering at us, or maybe because he was wearing me down, the cave-in feeling hits me the minute I let my guard down. I'm not going to tell anybody. Somehow saying it out loud would make it more scary, more real.

* * *

Friday. This afternoon I met the second surgeon, Dr. Martin. She came to the waiting room to get me wearing a smile and blue surgical scrubs, needing lipstick and a brush for her limp brown curls. I felt comfortable and knew instantly that I'd choose her.

Dr. Martin took me to her office and put my X-rays up on the lighted box. She pointed to the same gray spot Dr. Nagao had.

"This is a very large shadow. I don't think the entire mass is cancer but I'm certain that this is," she pointed to the darker area that looked like it had roots.

I have to admit that part looked very different from the rest of my breast. I looked at the X-ray and felt – how can I explain it? – like I was having two experiences at once. One was fear, mind-numbing fear. The other was me denying that it would turn out to be cancer but, at the same time, mentally planning what I need to do to make the lump go away before the surgery.

She went on to say that if the cancer hasn't spread inside my breast she'll do a lumpectomy. She does the needle localization, too, and for some reason it didn't sound quite so brutal this time. She said it won't really hurt. I don't believe her, though.

She said that if the lump is cancer and it's in other parts of my breast or if she can't get it all, I'll have to have a mastectomy. In that case, she's pretty sure my oncologist will recommend radiation and chemotherapy. Probably a follow-up drug called Tamoxifen, too.

I'm not used to feeling fear, probably have only felt this kind of fear twice in my life – once at the beach when Tricia was about three the tide pulled her away from me and I couldn't see her until the tide brought her back in, then once when she was older and we were at a water park the artificial waves swamped us and I thought I would drown trying to get her face above water. But those times the danger was over in a few minutes and the fear went away. This is different. I feel it building and I have to work to push it back down. I tell myself, *I do not have cancer. I will not need a mastectomy. I will not need radiation and chemotherapy.*

My mother died after cancer. Not from it, I remember specifically being told. The cancer markers were good but she was too weak from the chemotherapy to survive. She had a series of strokes, the chemo made her so weak she broke her back coughing! So weak she just didn't have the energy to recover. I'm trying to stay calm. *I do not have cancer. I will not need a mastectomy. I will not need radiation and chemotherapy. I know it will turn out that she's wrong. God knows, doctors are wrong all the time!*

I told Dr. Martin I'm going to visualize the lump going away and I'll use Reiki, and I asked her to do another X-ray in a few weeks. She said no, that I'll have the mammogram on the morning of the surgery and if the lump has disappeared, the surgery will be cancelled.

She booked me for a lumpectomy at Queen's Medical Center next week, October 16th. Her phone interrupted us and I waited while she talked to another doctor about an intern who did something during a surgery she wasn't happy about. I mentally thanked the Universe for this reminder – I don't want anyone practicing on me.

Don't worry, she said, and told me a phrase to add to my hospital authorization that will authorize only her to do the surgery.

"There's a possibility this isn't cancer, right?" I asked. I needed her to say yes.

She hesitated before saying, "A very small chance."

"I'm going to work on it," I told her. "Could you please remember a time when you were surprised that a tumor wasn't cancer and visualize being surprised about mine?"

She looked like I'd just suggested she visualize I would grow another arm but I don't care. I know visualization can work.

"I'm scheduled to teach a writing class the Saturday after surgery, do you think I should..."

"Cancel it," she said.

"But maybe it's not cancer..."

"You need to cancel the class."

I left her office and went straight to a used bookstore and bought a metaphysical book on healing by Robert Stone. His book has example after example of people who've used the power of their minds to get welland I know I'm as strong as any of them. I can do it too.

* * *

Sunday. I try to put fear out of my mind but it keeps worming its way back. I'm trying to be sure to spend time visualizing the lump being benign, or better yet, gone. I made myself a hypnosis tape about being cancer free. I listen to it several times a day and at night while I'm going to sleep.

I use Reiki while I'm driving and at night when I'm going to sleep. Is this what I learned Reiki for? When I first heard about it I didn't even know what energy healing was. Someone announced at a group meeting that there'd be an initiation to First Degree the following weekend and I just felt that it was something I was supposed to learn.

At the first part of the training the teacher explained that Reiki is a form of energy healing then she took us, four at a time, into another room where we sat in chairs in a row.

"This is very private," she said. "Close your eyes. Don't discuss your experience with anyone else."

I could hear her moving behind us, knew she was going from one of us to the next and the next. When she was behind me she placed her hands firmly on my head and I saw a flash of orange symbols against a black background. The palms of my hands got warm and she moved on to the woman on my left.

The palms of my hands still get warm whenever I think about Reiki or healing and when I use it on friends who have an injury they're always amazed that the pain pretty much goes away. I'm only at the first level, though. Maybe that isn't enough?

My friend Misha is a Reiki Master and he has a class coming up in late November. But that seems so far away. I feel I need to do whatever I can right away so I called to ask if he'd work with me in private sessions if I'll agree to attend the November class. I told him about the lump and that two doctors so far thought it was cancer. Bless his heart, he agreed to attune me on Thursday.

* * *

Tuesday morning. I had one of those conversations with myself about being so project driven. *What's the point of living in Hawaii if I'm never actually out in Hawaii?* I grabbed a bottle of water and drove 45 minutes into the country to Haleiwa for lunch. Relax, I told myself. Enjoy. Breathe.

The town is about a mile long and it's obvious the shops were built along its dusty main road without any kind of plan. There's a shop here and then there, old Hawaii wood buildings here, a cluster of modern stucco there, porch, no porch, sidewalk then not.

What Haleiwa lacks in street appeal it makes up for inside the shops. Great jewelry, trendy clothes I can't afford, local art, gemstones. Fujioka's market smells dusty but has a great wine selection and Matsumoto's, down the street, has tourists lined up outside the door to get shave ice. The best pizza on the island and the best hamburger in the world are in Haleiwa. At the east end there's a beach and a small marina where sail boats bob with the wind.

After lunch I drove to one of my favorite beaches, hunkered in my beach chair under the shade of some bushes and read.

Sometimes tourists stop at this beach, they climb down from the highway and are always alarmed when they see turtles the size of car tires "stranded" on the sand. They rush to the rescue. They talk soothingly and drench the turtles' shells with water from their children's plastic buckets; sometimes they try to coax them back to the ocean. Mostly, the turtles are patient.

I have to admit that I was rooting for the rescuers the first time. But these turtles live in the shallow water there, and they enjoy basking on the warm sand. When the tourists let them. The turtles were a good distraction but every once in a while my mind escaped the cocoon I try to keep it in. *What if I really do have cancer?*

Later. This evening Misha called with the name of a friend he wants me to talk to. She co-teaches his Reiki classes and he said he thought she might have some helpful information for me. I called her but she didn't tell me anything I didn't already know. I was ready to hang up when she asked how my family had taken the news.

"I haven't told anyone," I said. "I don't want them to worry before I know there's something to worry about."

"Aren't you going to tell your daughter?"

I said no, I don't want her to worry. She's in college in California, there's nothing she can do, and she needs to focus on school.

"You're being a bad mother if you don't tell her!" Kind of rude, I thought, considering she doesn't know me at all, but she went on.

"How would you like it if your daughter hid something like this from *you?*"

I had to admit that I wouldn't like it at all.

I called Tricia and tried not to cry when I told her. I tried to make it sound like I know it's worrisome but I also know it will turn out to be nothing but I think I'm more worried than I'm letting myself believe. She asked what she could do and I appreciate her offer but there really isn't anything she *can* do.

I also called my brother and my dad. No one knows quite what to say when you drop something like that on them. "Oh, no," they say. "What can I do?" But what *can* they do? Nothing, really.

* * *

Thursday. I went to Misha's and he spent three hours attuning me to Master Level Reiki, then he sent me out to the backyard to relax in the hammock. It felt strange but nice to just lie there, feeling the sun warm on my skin. I wonder what it would be like to not always be so busy, to have time to just lie around in the backyard. Technically, I have the time now. Why don't I do it? Because, of course, if I lie around, I won't have time to get everything else done.

Except for the palms of my hands, which feel even hotter than after the first level initiation, I don't notice a change. But I know it's there; *please, God, let it help.*

* * *

Friday. I called Sid, told him about the lump and asked if he'd take me to the hospital early Wednesday morning and pick me up in the afternoon. It will cost him an afternoon in the water and I was happy that he didn't hesitate for an instant before saying he would. He's a good ex-boyfriend. The water is actually one of the reasons he's my ex. I remember once early on when I was feeling squeezed in between his swimming, surfing, windsurfing and his yoga and aikido, telling him I didn't think he had time for me in his life. He was quick to say he knew that he did but he was telling me what he wanted to be true. The real truth is that we're better as friends.

* * *

Sunday. Today I went to two movies. Movies are good, they push other voices out of my head. Tonight I re-read Robert Stone's book. I talked to Tricia for a long time and felt sad when we hung up.

* * *

Monday. This morning on my way to work and the dreaded Monday morning meeting I noticed I wasn't breathing. I realized my body was clenched tight, my fingers had a strangle-hold on the steering wheel. I made a quick right turn and pulled over, sat there till I could relax some. I told myself this was crazy! It was only a meeting, for God's sake. Why couldn't I just let him do his silly meeting and not let it affect me? I turned around and drove for three or four minutes before I had to pull over again.

Okay, maybe I should be able to just let Gunther rant and rave without it affecting me but clearly, I can't. I drove home and called in sick. I'm proud of myself for paying attention to my body's distress and not pushing myself to ignore it. As a reward, I drove around the island and tried to think about happy things. I felt like I wanted to be around people so I stopped at Borders for awhile.

* * *

Tuesday. I told Gunther I'd been too stressed to come to work yesterday and he gave me a dirty look and said no problem but that I wouldn't get paid. I tried to focus on work and not let the angry energy of this place get to me but there's too much of it for me to ignore. I told Gunther and the owner about Thursday's surgery, that I'd be out till Monday, and left.

* * *

Wednesday. I'm afraid but trying not to be. I am refusing to consider the worst case scenario and spent the whole day reading Stone's book.

* * *

Thursday. This morning Sid dropped me off with a hug at Queen's Medical Center much earlier than either of us like to be awake. We'd already agreed that there wasn't anything he could do so he went on to work.

I signed in and I was sent to have my blood pressure taken (low like always) and my arm jabbed (blood work normal). The technician was in a chatty mood and for some reason she told me all about her recent breast reduction surgery. All through this I was surprisingly calm.

Next, I was wheeled (!!!) upstairs for the needle localization procedure. They gave me a gown to change into and led me to a chair in the middle of the room (not quite so calm). An assistant stood behind me, letting me use her soft body as a headrest (in case I fainted?) while the doctor consulted my X-ray. I closed my eyes and focused on my breathing as he inserted a large, long needle into my breast. Dr. Martin was right, it didn't really hurt much.

"If I were a betting man I'd be 99 percent certain that this isn't cancer," he said looking at the mammogram film.

See, Dr. Martin, I told you! I wanted to hug him, dance around the room, run down to surgery and tell her what he'd said.

Instead, I let myself be wheeled to the "holding" area, the crowded and noisy corridor where patients wait to be taken to an operating room. There's no privacy, just a thin cotton curtain between patients and I was glad I'd brought my tape player to drown out their voices. I clamped the headset against my ears and tried to pay attention to messages I'd taped about being calm, about having my pulse and blood pressure normal, about having the surgery go smoothly.

When the anesthesiologist came by I asked him to please keep my tapes playing and he promised he would. Finally it was my turn and my heart started drumming hard and fast. They rolled me down the hall, into a room and helped me slip onto the operating table. One last plea to God then I was unconscious.

I was still groggy when Sid came to pick me up. Dr. Martin doesn't share post-surgery information till the pathologist has done his final work so we won't hear the news till my appointment tomorrow morning.

When we got back to my apartment my guard dropped and I was afraid – what if I *do* have cancer? I didn't want to be alone so Sid agreed to stay with me for awhile.

* * *

Friday. This morning I felt a little better. Not so afraid. Sid took me to see Dr. Martin and afterwards I was going to take him to lunch to say thanks and to celebrate not having cancer. I had a really nice restaurant picked out.

I stepped into the waiting room, smiled at Dr. Martin's receptionist and felt a small cave-in in my chest. She had always been nice to me and I was pretty sure she was uncomfortable. I tried to make it my imagination. Dr. Martin came into the waiting room to get me before I'd even had a chance to sit down.

"So," I said smiling at her, "good news, right?" Her face relaxed to sadness. "I'm so sorry, no."

No? Oh, no! One minute I was happy and the next minute I was trying to understand that I'm going to die. I'll be leaving Tricia, my wonderful daughter, my wonderful best friend. I won't get to see her graduate from college. Won't be here to see her get married someday, and have a baby. I won't find my soul mate and enjoy his love. I won't get to write all those other books I want to write. Everyone I've ever known who's had cancer has died and now I'm going to die, too.

Somehow I followed her into the examination room and went through the physical motions of taking off my shirt and folding it neatly. Like that mattered. She examined the incision and shook her head sadly at how nicely it was already mending. I know she was thinking, *what a waste. It will all come off with the mastectomy and later she will die.* Dr. Martin told me to get dressed and meet her in her office. Somehow I managed to.

She was sitting at a large wooden desk. On the credenza behind her a CD player played soft New Age music. A brown teddy bear sat by the CD player – a gift or something to soften the room? There were two chairs facing her desk and Sid was in the one by the wall. I knew the other was for me and for an instant I considered doing what was expected of me but then did what I wanted to do instead. I passed the empty chair and climbed into Sid's lap and buried my head in his chest. Then I sobbed. It was all I could do. Sid cried more quietly.

Dr. Martin explained and drew pictures and from time to time I stopped sobbing to ask a question. Most of what she said I forgot two minutes later. But some parts stuck "…cancer…6+ centimeters…unfortunately, not the good kind, invasive lobular carcinoma in situ, aggressive…no guarantees, but best chance for survival are mastectomy, chemotherapy, radiation, Tamoxifen…."

She explained that she hadn't gotten clean margins – meaning that when she took out the part that was cancer it wasn't completely surrounded by healthy tissue. She took more and still didn't get completely clean margins. She said that she'd cauterized the area and sometimes that kills the cells that are still there and sometimes the body is able to kill the stragglers with its own defenses, but that I can't count on it.

I can't believe I'm going to have to have a mastectomy. It sounds like such a drastic, brutal thing to have to do if there are only a few cells left and even she says those might already be gone. I asked her if she couldn't just go back and get the rest of it but she was insistent, I have to have a mastectomy and she wants to do it right away. She tells me that time is important, that it's dangerous to wait too long after the cells have been disturbed.

The good news, she said, smiling sort of, is that even though I don't look like I need it, I'll get a tummy tuck free when they do the reconstructive surgery. She thinks that the oncologist will want to wait a few years though, because it's easier to spot recurrence if the chest (MY CHEST!!!) is flat.

I've talked vaguely about getting a tummy tuck if I ever needed other abdominal surgery but I didn't want one this way!

She wanted me to let her make an appointment for a mastectomy, saying I can always cancel if I change my mind. I feel like I was being pushed, I *was,* but I said okay. I'm afraid, I don't want to die, I don't know what else to do.

Her outside wall is glass and I looked at Honolulu some 800 feet below, marveling at how the city can be so unchanged while my life has been changed drastically.

She handed me two pieces of paper and I went downstairs by myself to have a cancer titer blood test and a chest X-ray. She didn't need to say why; she wants to see if it's spread. I couldn't stop crying; I knew my mascara was running, my eyes were red. People were looking but I didn't care. I fumbled for the elevator button to the basement and walked down a long hall. I blinked to clear the tears from my eyes and turned into the X-ray room. I could barely get the words out, *I have cancer.* The technician's face softened, she took the authorization slip and led me to a changing room. After the X-ray I had the blood test.

Sid and I didn't go to lunch. We went back to my apartment and cried some more. He stayed and we slept fitfully, T-shirt and shorts pressed tight against T-shirt and shorts.

* * *

Saturday. Sid left about 4 a.m. and when I woke up again I was alone with a speaker blaring in my head: *I have cancer. Like my mother. She did everything the doctors wanted her to do and she died.*

I feel so helpless. I've never felt so overwhelmed and alone before. In the 16 years I've been single I've had some tough things to deal with but nothing like this. All I want to do is cry and sleep. And so that's all I'm doing.

In the old days hospitals had strict visiting hours and strict rules about what went on in the rooms. Now they're much more lenient and I've always thought that when I'm dying I'd want to have someone I love in bed with me, holding me. It looks like that might be happening soon.

I'm grateful for the weekend, I couldn't have gone to work today if my life depended on it. My mind races, my heart pounds, my body shakes. Between fear and uncertainty, I haven't eaten much at all and I'm starting to lose weight. Not a bad thing, but not the diet plan I'd have chosen.

Even though I don't really believe in astrology, I keep thinking about a friend who did my chart. She said that if I didn't change my eating habits I'd have a serious illness in 10 years and that was exactly 10 years ago. I've eaten junk, the more sugar and fat the better, since the 8th grade. In school, the cafeteria had yummy desserts and lots of times my lunch was two pieces of pie and a piece of cake. Even now...well...last month, before all this, I'd go grocery shopping and end up with two empty Butterfinger wrappers at the check-out. Or two wrappers left over from bakery donuts. I've wanted to change but it's like an addiction. Now, I have a life-and-death-strong reason to change. I believe that basically a person's body knows how to be healthy and I've sabotaged mine by eating food it can't use to keep me well. I have to stop eating junk food and I will. Right now.

But I don't know what I *should* eat. I've lived on empty-calorie packaged frozen dinners for so long that I can't think of anything healthy that sounds good. I don't like very many vegetables, I don't eat chicken or meat – how many ways can I cook the three fish I know anything about?

I know that stress triggers a person's body to produce cortisol and that lowers the immune system so I'm reluctant to go back to work on Monday. I've been constantly under stress for a whole year. Gunther is the worst boss I've ever had in my life. *WHY HAVEN'T I QUIT?* One day he asked if he could talk to me out on the porch. He said the owner said it was his fault all the other sales reps quit and he thought it was her policies. What did I think? I told him I thought it was both of their faults. The same day the owner asked me to meet *her* out on the porch and she asked me the same question. I told her the same thing. But nothing changes.

* * *

Sunday. This afternoon I went to Sedona, a shop in Ward Center, and asked a clerk which stones are good for healing. I bought enough for a bracelet. Some people survive cancer. I asked if anyone there knew of a doctor who treated cancer holistically but nobody did. I went to Borders and looked in the alternative medicine section for cancer cookbooks that will at least tell me what to eat.

* * *

Monday. This morning at work I told the receptionist matter-of-factly that I have cancer, that I have to have a mastectomy, but that I'm going to fight to survive. Kerri let the phones ring and gave me high-five and said she's proud of me. I told the owner and she was sympathetic. I told her I really didn't want to have a mastectomy and asked what she thought she'd do in my shoes.

"My dad was a surgeon," she said "and I'd do whatever the physicians suggested."

Gunther came by and said in his smarmy voice that he's so sorry. I nodded and turned away. I know I shouldn't, but I blame him for the stress that's weakened my body so the cancer could invade.

The rest of the day I kept busy so I wouldn't have to think. I came straight home from work and tried to think of options to the mastectomy. I've always said that doctors are good for broken bones and sore throats but if something really bad ever happened I'd go to a natural healer. Well, this is something really bad. I just can't see cutting, poisoning and burning me as the first step to making me well. Especially if there are only one or two cells and even those might be gone! I have to find a doctor who will make me well without practically killing me first.

But then I hear Dr. Martin's voice saying my cancer is very large, invasive, aggressive, my best chance for survival is...and I tell myself if I choose wrong, chances are very good I'll die. What should I do?

* * *

Tuesday. Dr. Martin's office called to say the chest X-ray report came back fine but that Dr. Martin wants me to have a baseline liver/spleen scan and a bone scan. I know why.

I called Misha and asked him if he knew any holistic doctors. He said no, but invited me to his birthday party Saturday. He says a doctor friend of his from the Big Island will be there, I should find him, tell him what's going on and ask what he thinks I should do.

I've heard that doctors are doing more innovative medicine in Europe so I called Sheila to ask her to find out what they're doing in England. She was pretty surprised to get a phone call from me and sounded shocked when I told her I have cancer. I guess I've known her longer than anyone, since 7th grade, and even though we just started out as pen pals we became good friends ages ago. She promised to ask around and call me back.

Tonight I went dancing at Pecos River Café, one of the few places on the island where we can dance two-step and west coast swing. I told the people in my dancing group that I've been diagnosed with breast cancer and they are all sorry, said all the right things. Some promised to pray for me. One encouraged me to talk to Kathy, the Kathy I know from dancing, who they say had cancer two or three years ago and seems fine.

Larry was there, a guy I'd spotted at Rumours several Friday nights ago, and we danced some. He's tall, cute and a good dancer. It was nice to be able to block the cancer out and have fun.

* * *

Wednesday. One week after surgery. This morning I took off a couple of hours from work to have the scans done. For the liver/spleen test they injected a dye and told me to come back in an hour. Hard to relax when I knew what they were looking for.

I'm hoping either the oncologist or the radiation therapists Dr. Martin recommended will be able to help me find a less damaging way to get rid of these straggler cells so this morning I sat in Dr. Cho's chilly examining room, feeling captive in a mini-gown in a mini-room. He used the same words Dr. Martin had, "...no guarantee... your best chance for survival...." I can just feel the energy, the life, being sucked out of me whenever I hear that.

He acknowledged that yes, the chemotherapy is dangerous, yes, I will lose my hair, and no, there are no guarantees that a) I need it or b) I will survive. He read his notes and reminded me that I had invasive lobular cancer, the aggressive kind, that the margins hadn't been clean, blah, blah, blah.

I asked him if he couldn't please help me find a holistic way to treat this but he said there isn't one.

It took two hours for my body to let go of that doomed feeling. Tricia called and I told her what the oncologist said.

"I'll come stay with you after the mastectomy if you want me to," she offered.

"What about your job? Would they let you off?"

"Probably not, but I'll quit." She's just found a part-time job to help with her college bills and I don't want her to lose it but I appreciate her offer more than I can say.

I told her let's wait and see. We talked till it was time for her to go to work.

"I love you, Mom," she said. "Here's a hug, can you feel it?" I closed my eyes and I could feel her arms around me, I could actually feel the fear slip away.

* * *

Thursday. I got a care package from Tricia filled with wonderful cheering-up gifts: a Yoda Pez dispenser (Yoda is my role model), a children's paint box, a bottle of bubbles and a can of scented spray that promises to lift the energy of a room. She's a gift herself.

When I'm not at work I'm digging for information. I've combed the phone book looking for holistic doctors, called a few whose idea of holistic medicine turned out to be encouraging meditation while you're undergoing chemotherapy or using guided imagery to deal with stress. That's not enough.

I've found listings for Hawaiian healers who do whatever magic they do, but I don't trust that. There are dozens of Chinese doctors in Honolulu, with their jars of herbs and teas, but I don't know how to choose a good one. I just want a regular M.D. who will work with me a little, help me be well without harming me first. Every day I am closer to having to have a mastectomy because I can't find a doctor who has any other ideas.

Meanwhile, I try to focus on work. Michael, one of my clients, is a metaphysical man and I told him that I've had cancer and am scheduled for a mastectomy.

He begged me to please not do it till I've explored other options.

I told him I've *looked*, but I can't *find* any options.

"I've got a video tape I'd like you to watch on oxygen therapy. Cancer can't grow when there's enough oxygen in your cells. Oxygen therapy creates a climate that is *inhospitable* to cancer."

I asked if that's what he'd do if he had cancer.

"Absolutely." I agreed to watch the tape, even though I think it sounds pretty hokey.

Later I spent two hours talking with Dr. Spagliani. Mostly, she talked. She spent two whole hours trying to convince me that I should have radiation. I wouldn't have imagined there were that many words to say about the subject. I kept asking her if there isn't *any* other way to treat my cancer and she kept saying no, then repeating the depressing survival figures for people with my kind of cancer. She seems to earnestly care but I remind myself that isn't the point. The point is – what really *is* the best thing for *me*? I was depressed again for several hours.

I know what *isn't* good for me is stress and the stress of having to be around Gunther and having cancer and probably dying is just too much. I realized that my most important job right now is not selling, but investigating ways to survive. I went back to the office, threw a few personal things from my desk into a brown envelope, went into the owner's office, told her I was taking a leave of absence and walked out.

After lunch I spent several hours at Borders, then went to Barnes & Noble looking for books on alternative care. I read through one about a doctor in South Texas who seems to have a program that works but he doesn't seem to work much with breast cancer. I read about a lady who cured herself with a diet strictly of carrot juice. Not for me. Another woman, here on Oahu, writes that she cured her cancer with major amounts of exercise. These things sound too one-dimensional. I believe it will take more than one thing to make my body well.

I bought *Love, Medicine and Miracles* by Bernie Siegel. Great book, and my first encouragement from anyone with M.D. after their name to play an active part in my wellness.

Tonight I heard the words again. They popped into my head for the first time last week. *It's time to go.* Does that mean me? Does it mean I'm going to die? I don't like it. I know that, except for Tricia, I don't have any strong reason to be around. I don't have a job I like, I don't have a relationship, I live in paradise and it's pleasant but I'm not having any fun.... I miss having friends I can laugh with. But Tricia is enough reason to stay, so I *can't* go....

* * *

Friday. Queen's Medical Center makes you pre-register before any overnight surgery so this morning I dragged myself over there so they could confirm my insurance and make sure I understand the operation. A nurse spent half an hour talking to me about the surgery, about having to wear a drainage tube and how to empty it. About half way through her talk, I became nauseated and terrified.

But I'm such a trouper. I showed up that afternoon for my appointment with Dr. Martin to go over the surgery. The New Age music was on in her office again and she took some papers out of my folder. I asked her why she *has* to do a mastectomy? Why can't she just go back and get clean margins? She says taking more tissue would compromise the success of reconstruction. I can't imagine why, there seems to be plenty of skin there. I asked her again, I pleaded with her, "isn't there *any* other way we can treat this?"

"I wish there was. Don't you think I'd love to tell you there is? Don't you think if there were that every wealthy movie star, every politician would take advantage of it? There just isn't."

"Yes, but..." She interrupted me. "You need to remember that the cancer you had was the aggressive kind and that there's no guarantee you'll survive even *with* the mastectomy, radiation and chemotherapy. But you're young and vital and that is what will give you the best chance."

She wants me to think the surgery isn't that big a deal and says most of her patients go back to work a few days after a mastectomy and work through chemo without a problem. Maybe. I know there are women who suffer treatments bravely and they survive, women who wear a wig like a badge of courage and women anxious to have not only their cancerous breast removed but the healthy breast, too. I guess, I *hope*, they do what they do because they feel it's the right thing to do. But I am not any of those women. I feel so strongly that, for me, it isn't.

While I was in her office, a patient called and asked if it was okay to get her hair done the day before her mastectomy. I tried to wrap my mind around this concept. She was having somewhat major surgery in which she would lose an important part of her body and she wanted to make sure *her hair looked good?*

The lady got to have her hair done and Dr. Martin turned back to me. She said she had to tell me the things that could go wrong during and after the surgery. First, since she'll be taking the lymph nodes in my right armpit, I'll need to be sure not to put my right hand anywhere it'd be at risk of infection. That means I shouldn't reach into the oven with my right hand (it could be burned and without the lymph system intact it could become infected), I shouldn't play dangerous games with my right hand (it could be scratched or cut and become infected), I shouldn't have my blood drawn or blood pressure taken on my right arm (???).

I asked her again, couldn't she just go back and take a little more and get clean margins? She said no.

She looked back down at her notes and mentioned a condition called lymphedema, which is when fluid is retained. This could cause my right arm to swell and be larger than my left. But she added that there are wraps I can wear to help keep the swelling down. Last, but certainly not least, this stunner: The unlikely but possible condition where for some reason I don't understand my right shoulder blade might pop out and I'll look like I've sprouted a single wing. I sat there for a minute dumbfounded. She waited. Finally I signed the papers, but the entire time my body was screaming at me no, NO, **NO, NO!**

One of the lessons I learned years ago when I was refinancing my house was not to make a decision out of fear. But I'm doing it. All of these doctors are pushing me to. They're doing their best to scare the shit out of me and I tell you what, it's working. My body locks tight with dread and fear whenever I talk to them but I haven't totally given in.

I stopped by a health food store run by a friend and asked her if she knew of an alternative doc here on the island (she doesn't). I go online, I scour the bookstores and I notice how different I feel – I'm optimistic, I feel powerful and light at the same time when I think about finding a way to get well without damaging my body.

I have moments, briefly, when I feel strong enough to cancel the mastectomy but then fear washes back over me. I really do want to survive this. If I do decide not to have the surgery I want to be completely educated about what I'm saying no to. Next week I have an appointment with a second doctor to talk about radiation.

The Cancer Society has a buddy program where they match you with someone who's had the same cancer and treatment that you're facing. I'm not really interested, but one of my friends says I should give it a chance. This afternoon my buddy called but her surgeon had gotten clean margins, she didn't have a mastectomy and she was happy following doctors' orders so her situation is nothing like mine. I don't see how she can help. I told her thanks, but I don't think I'll be interested.

Tonight I went dancing at Rumours to be social and to try to pull my thoughts away from cancer. Most of my dance friends were there and Kathy was there, too. I told her about the cancer and mastectomy and asked her about her experience.

She said four years ago, late April, she found a lump in her right breast. She got two or three opinions and since there was cancer in so many sites, she agreed to have a mastectomy in early May. Lymph nodes were removed and that showed the cancer hadn't spread but she was given chemotherapy to be safe. She said she had four treatments of Adriamycin, a really aggressive medicine that is hard on the heart and she was told she could never have it again. The Adriamycin was mixed with Cytoxin 5 and they gave her Zofran to combat nausea. She had her final chemo dose in August.

Before Christmas, just eight months after her first surgery, she could see another lump. It was removed and she was given 35 treatments of radiation over a seven-week period. This, she said, caused slight damage to her lung. She was finished with the radiation in March 1994 but in September there was *another lump!* This didn't fit any protocol – with each surgery there'd been clean margins. After her doctor consulted with a doctor on the mainland, he did one more surgery, this time in his office with just Novocaine.

By this time, Kathy said, she'd decided that what the doctors were doing wasn't working. She swore she'd die before she had chemo again so she decided to change her diet – no dairy, no meat, fat free. She discovered a nutritionist who did a live blood analysis, then recommended supplements based on what she saw. Kathy took the supplements the dietitian recommended and told me she'd been fine now for three years. She's not sure whether the doctors finally got all the cancer or whether her new diet, digestive enzymes and other supplements had made the difference. She gave me the dietitian's number and I promised to make an appointment.

* * *

Friday night. Dance-guy Larry invited me out for dinner, ta da! He's really nice, and fun in a laid-back way. I'm pretty busy right now so it wouldn't be a good time to get really interested in someone. But still....

* * *

Saturday. Afternoon. I called Michael and went to pick up the oxygen tape he wants me to watch. I'm pretty skeptical but I told him I'd watch it so I will. He's a little more comfortable with the mastectomy since I told him my surgeon is a woman but he still told me a story about when his dad was in pre-med. He said his dad overheard doctors saying they were going to talk Mrs. So-and-So into a gallbladder surgery to help finance a trip to Europe; they were going to talk Mrs. Whoosits into a hysterectomy to finance their kids' school tuition. Michael said it happened so often that his dad dropped out of medical school, disgusted.

* * *

Sunday. Last night I went to Misha's birthday party at a friend's house in Waimanalo. I like local communities and I think if my life were slower I'd like living here and getting to know the people. Maybe they could teach me how to relax. I wouldn't like the drive to Honolulu, though, too far.

I parked and then stood by my car a few minutes. The night was quiet except for the ocean lapping up against rocks across the road. I looked on down the street at the row of wood houses up on wooden supports. How many floods have they protected the homes against? I watched the rows of palm trees gently swaying in the breeze and wondered about the words I still hear sometimes, about it being time to go. Why would I want to leave all this? I love living in Hawaii.

There was a lively canine greeting committee at the gate but I pushed past, found Misha and gave him a birthday hug. He pointed out his doctor friend from the Big Island and I went over and introduced myself.

"I've just been diagnosed with cancer," I said, "and Misha says I should talk to you."

"Let's go for a walk on the beach," he said. "Tell me everything." We crossed the street, I slipped my sandals off and let my toes sink into the sand, still warm even though the sun was down. I watched the waves roll in and out in a calming pattern and told him what Dr. Martin had said.

"I was fine having the lumpectomy. I agreed the lump didn't belong there. But they're saying I have to have a mastectomy, do chemo and radiation and it just feels too damaging. She doesn't know for sure that there's even any cancer left."

He thought for a minute then said, "I agree, having the lump removed was definitely the right thing to do. But before you do anything else, there's a book you should read. It's edited by Burton Goldberg and you need to read it before you make any more decisions." He couldn't remember the title but said it lists the protocols of about 30 doctors who are having good results with alternative medicine. He's loaned his copy to his sister but said he'll call her Monday to see if she's ready to give it back.

I asked him if there are any doctors in Hawaii who

can help me with holistic therapy and he said that, unfortunately, he doesn't know any.

I told him that Dr. Martin says we need to move quickly with the mastectomy but he says he doesn't think waiting an extra week or two while I explore my options will increase my risk.

Cancer was all that was on my mind so when another man at the party innocently asked how I was I told him.

"Get the mastectomy," he said.

"I went with a lady a while. She told me she had a breast missing and I said it didn't matter. And it didn't."

Okay, but I thought about Sid, as honorable a man as I know, and when I'd asked him if it would matter if someone he loved had a mastectomy there'd been a significant pause before he'd said he hoped it wouldn't. That's not encouraging but it's not the point; even if it wouldn't matter to a significant other, it would matter to *me*.

* * *

Monday. This morning I went to see the dietitian Kathy told me about. Mary Lou showed me a magnified drop of my live blood and said it's too clumped, there's not enough oxygen, it's a good nest for cancer cells to grow in. Oxygen? I need to watch that tape.

"You need to exercise more," she said. "And there's a lot of sugar in your blood – cancer loves sugar."

She said there are also a lot of uric acid crystals in my blood and the natural killer cells that are supposed to gobble cancer cells get so busy gobbling the remains of yesterday's fatty muffins and the ice cream from the day before that they don't get around to the cancer cells. I'm impressed with the blood test. I wonder why doctors don't do it. She told me to take digestive enzymes and she recommended a couple of the same supplements Kathy takes. There's also a tea called Essiac, that she says has been linked with cancer cures. I bought some tea, some digestive enzymes and a couple of other supplements. I promised to take them for a few days then come back for another blood test.

Mary Lou told me about another client of hers who'd had cancer and had gone to a clinic in Mexico. She's also heard good things about a wellness retreat near San Diego in California called Optimum Health Institute and thinks her client/friend went there, too. The lady gave Mary Lou permission to give out her phone number so I took it and promised to call. This feels good. Doors seem to be opening. Maybe this is the first step toward what I'm looking for.

I've read things about cancer treatment centers in Mexico and it seems like it could be a possibility for me, but a slim one. But San Diego, no medicines, just diet... that feels comfortable.

Mary Lou asked if I knew about Caroline Myss and when I said I didn't, she loaned me her own personal set of Myss tapes.

She asked if I knew about the cancer book by Burton Goldberg...turns out it's the same book Misha's doctor-friend told me about! I love how the same messages come to me from different places – like the Universe is making sure I don't miss them.

Almost as a "by the way...," she told me about a naturopath in Aiea who works with cancer patients. I don't know much about naturopaths, I'd rather work with an M.D., but if I can't maybe this will work. Actually, the more I think about it, the more I think that maybe this is what I've been looking, praying for! She didn't have his phone number but she wrote his name down for me. A holistic doctor! I couldn't wait to go home and call him.

But first I had to go to my appointment with the second radiotherapy doctor. He quoted the same grim message about "this kind of cancer," and "best chances for survival." I asked him if there isn't *any* other way to deal with this cancer?

He told me this wouldn't be his first choice, but if I absolutely refuse to have chemotherapy he'll be willing to do only radiation. He says he really thinks I need to do both but one would be better than nothing.

I asked him about the dangers, about healthy tissue being burned and Kathy's lung being injured and he admitted that it happens, that there are dangers.... I left feeling depressed but tried to cheer myself up by thinking about calling the naturopath. I got home and went through the entire Yellow Pages looking for him but he's not there. I checked the White Pages, not there. I called information and they couldn't find him, either. He must have left the island. I feel like someone threw me a life raft and it sank before I could get to it.

I am so disappointed. There actually was a doctor here but he's not here now. I try to tell myself it's just a bump in the road.

I like the live blood analysis but don't feel I should put all my eggs in that basket. I'm confused and sometimes angry. I get such strong gut feelings that I shouldn't have this surgery but the Universe, God, isn't giving me anything to help me stop it. I'm running out of time.

Larry, the dance guy, invited me to dinner at his place tonight. I tried to push the cancer to the back of my mind and go have fun. Pretty cool, tall, flirty and cute, and he can cook! His condo overlooks a cemetery and he told

me his sister is there. I've told him about my breast cancer and he was vague about how she died then changed
the subject right away so I figure she probably had breast
cancer, too. He also told me about a woman he's not sure
he's over. Red alert, red alert, I can't get interested in him.
My emotions are already on a roller-coaster ride, I can't
afford to start to like somebody who might not really be
available. I don't need more stress.

* * *

Tuesday. I watched Michael's tape about oxygen
therapy, basically an info-promotional video that claims
that since cancer can't live in an oxygenated climate, the
way to eliminate cancer is to oxygenate your body's cells
so the cancer will die. Mary Lou hasn't said anything
about oxygen therapy but she told me my blood cells
are clumped, unoxygenated, and that cancer thrives in
that kind of climate. The video looked very scientific
and actually made a lot of sense. I noticed I felt calm and
peaceful. Is this too easy to believe or have I finally been
led to a non-destructive therapy to treat cancer? And if
there's one, aren't the chances good that there are others?
About half way through the video I felt my body shift into
hopeful optimism mode. I think I need to take more time
looking before I let something happen to me that still feels
so wrong.

I called Dr. Martin, told her I wanted to cancel the
surgery and caught myself holding my breath while she
answered.

"I can give you a short period of time to make a
final decision and if you still decline the mastectomy I'll
have to send you a registered letter confirming that you
have chosen not to follow the recommended protocol.
You'll need to sign it and send it back to me. You're so
young and vital, I hate to see you take such a risk."

Aaarg. Just talking to her on the phone leaves me feeling heavy and depressed. I forced myself to breathe again and spent the next hour curled up on the couch with the phone book, looking at doctors' names, trying to intuit who might have some interest and skill in alternative medicine. I called a dozen but none did.

I went to a friend's who has Internet and looked up alternative medicine and there seems to be a fair amount written about it. There's a group in California and I called the number they listed. The woman I talked to is supportive, a cancer survivor herself, but she doesn't really have any specific cure to tell me about.

She told me that sometimes drug companies do test studies, where they put women on medications they hope will work. But the downside is that if you agree to participate there's no guarantee that you'll be selected for the actual drug. You might be put in the group that takes a placebo and you'll never know.

A few days ago my friend Jennifer invited me to a meeting tonight, said maybe it would help take my mind off my troubles. We drove up to Mililani and I love how things work out – literally the first thing I heard inside the front door was a woman telling someone that she'd just found a wonderful naturopath. Ta da, it was the doctor Mary Lou told me about! The lady showed me his card and I realized why I haven't been able to find him. We've all been spelling his name wrong.

* * *

Wednesday. I called the naturopath, Dr. Pfeil, at 9 a.m. and a chorus of angels sang in the background – no, not really, but in a movie they would have.

I told the receptionist that I'd recently been diagnosed with breast cancer and that I'm looking for an alternative care doctor to help me get rid of anything left, if there is anything left. I asked if Dr. Pfeil had experience with cancer patients?

She said yes, he's worked with a lot of cancer patients, but he doesn't have an opening for a new patient for two months!!!

My heart and the *second* life raft sank. I explained my situation and asked what she thought about his experience and track record with cancer patients and she said she was trusting him with *her* life. She'd had breast cancer, too. She promised to rearrange some appointments and get me in as soon as she can.

After lunch I called Mary Lou's client/friend Rebecca and drove over to Kailua to meet her. Rebecca says she had cancer and went to the Mexico clinic. She thinks it's very reputable but the disadvantage is that you have to go back at least once a year for checkups. Pretty expensive when you live in Hawaii.

I asked what she thought about the fact that Steve McQueen went to Mexico for treatment and died and she said he went too late. She said most of the time when we hear those stories the people have given traditional medicine a long try and have already been diagnosed as terminal. They give Mexico a final chance and sometimes it works but sometimes it's just too late.

She's also been to the Optimum Health Institute and said if I didn't go to Mexico, I should definitely go there. Mary Lou told me she knew a doctor who worked there and she'd give me his name if I decided to go. Maybe I should.

Rebecca brought a book to loan me and, chuh ching, it's the same book both Misha's doctor friend and Mary Lou told me about! *Burton Goldberg Presents an Alternative Medicine Definitive Guide to Cancer.* And below the main title, "*Cancer Can Be* **Reversed***. This Book Tells How,*

Using Clinically Proven Complementary and Alternative Therapies." I felt a real rush of optimism when I saw it. That's the second time the Institute has popped up and the third time for the book. I've learned that when I get multiple messages like this I'm supposed to pay attention.

I called Kathy and we talked for nearly an hour about radiation and mastectomies, nutrition and alternative care. She said the mastectomy wasn't really that bad and offered to let me see her scar. She said her prosthesis is so good no one can tell. That's great, but....

I catch myself looking into the bathroom mirror, asking myself seriously, *am I resisting Dr. Martin's treatment simply because I'm vain?* Of course I don't want to have a scar instead of a breast but am I willing to give up my life for it?

Is it about losing my hair? I think I look pretty good for my age, my pale blonde tousled look is perfect for me. I know I'd make a really ugly bald person. But is that what's holding me back?

I stare into my eyes and honestly don't think so. I think about my mother's cancer "cure." I just feel in my body that this treatment is wrong for me. Maybe if I had raging cancer...but I don't have raging cancer. At most, I have a few cells and Dr. Martin admits they might already be gone!

Speaking of...she called again and I tried to keep breathing while she warned me again what statistics show for my kind of cancer...and that "even *with* the mastectomy, chemo and radiation there was no guarantee..." that "it's important for me to at least give them a chance...." She did say, though, that the chest X-ray was clear and that the bone scan came out fine. Except that there was a shadow on my brain. She doesn't think it's cancer, but maybe we should follow up with a brain scan?

I told her that at this point I'm not going to have radiation or chemo so there probably isn't any reason to follow up. She was quiet for a minute then reminded me she'll have to send me a letter pretty soon. She's trying to scare me and she does. Every time. I decided I needed to surround myself with nature so I grabbed Goldberg's book and drove to Kaimana Beach. Amazing, even though it's just a few blocks east of Waikiki, tourists hardly ever go there so it's never crowded. I like being one of the locals, basking in the sun. I found a spot in the shade of a palm tree and set up my chair.

I used to come here a lot when I first moved to Hawaii. When I was writing the Christmas book I came here to edit and it's still one of my favorite beaches. The sun was warm. A gentle breeze blew softly against my skin. All I had to do was raise my eyes to see endless blue ocean.

I watched the surfers for a minute then opened the book. After just a few pages, realized I was holding a goldmine.

Goldberg's book is amazing, 1,116 pages of great information! He presents very detailed protocols from M.D.s in Arizona, California, Colorado, Florida, Georgia, Illinois, Nevada, New Jersey and New York; M.D.s in England, Canada and Mexico, and also from Naturopathic Doctors in Oregon and Washington and a Chiropractor in Illinois. Every one of these 23 doctors seems to have a well-thought-out program and good success rates for treating cancer patients holistically, only resorting to chemo and radiation as a last resort. I feel like my prayers have been answered. If I can believe this book – and there are pictures of these doctors, credentials that are pretty impressive – there are *lots* of ways to treat cancer. The only bad part is that none of them is in Hawaii. But I tell myself that's okay, at least I've been shown that what I want to do can be done.

I drove to Barnes & Noble in Kahala to look for a copy of the book for myself but they didn't have it. I went to Down to Earth but they didn't have it and if they don't, no other health food store will. I called Borders, they don't have it. Ditto Waldenbooks. One of the advantages of living on a small island is that if you look for something four or five places and don't find it, it probably isn't here.

* * *

Thursday. I woke up feeling oddly calm. My shoulders didn't tense up around my ears like they usually do. Today I was supposed to have a mastectomy and thank God I'm not. I spent the morning back at the beach, reading Goldberg's book and thinking about my conversation with Rebecca. After about an hour I packed up and drove home, called San Diego to see what the Optimum Health Institute is all about.

I found out they serve raw fruits and vegetables, mostly juiced, three meals a day, they grow their own wheat grass on the premises, have daily exercise programs and lectures during the day on a variety of wellness subjects that guests are encouraged to attend.

There are also massage therapists on the premises (to help drain lymphatic fluids), extra fee, though. The whole program is designed to cleanse your body of the junk it's accumulated. I've certainly put a lot of junk food in my body that I could stand getting rid of. I felt very relaxed talking to the lady at the Institute, something I'm learning to notice when I'm about to make a decision.

The Institute likes you to stay three weeks but I feel comfortable committing to two. Their week starts on Sundays and I don't see any reason to wait so I booked a private room and told them I'll be there this Sunday. I have two days to wrap things up here and pack. Just a thought: Why do I always need to wrap things up? Why can't I just go? Leave things in whatever state they're in, walk out, then start back where I left off when I get back?

I used to be calm. When, how did I develop this need to...what?...to be so busy, to get everything done? I wrote a book on job survival, for God's sake, reminding readers that It Will NEVER All Get Done but I still push myself and feel anxious when I think about stopping without bringing some order to what I'm working on. It's probably the same thing that drives me to overwork at work. Even though my bosses never appreciate all the extra work I do. Even my clients don't appreciate it that much, I don't think.

Why do I care who appreciates what? Is this my childhood butting in? Trying to get the approval I never got as a child? I'm sure there's something I'm supposed to learn from all this...what is it? To let go? But what about goals, drive, don't you have to work hard to succeed? Yikes! I hear my dad lecturing me that life isn't easy, you have to work hard.... I remember mentally saying that wasn't the way *my* life was going to be. But it is. Maybe I can sort some of this out in California.

I called Dad to ask if I could borrow money from my inheritance to pay for the stay and the naturopathic medications since my insurance won't and was happily surprised when he said he would just give me the money for it.

The next few hours are a blur. Why can't I do anything slowly? I called the airlines, booked a flight to Los Angeles (much cheaper than flying directly into San Diego), booked a rental car, called my editor/friend Julie to see if I could stay overnight Saturday with her; called my old dance-buddy Art to see if we can get together to dance in Los Angeles after I leave the Institute. And I called Tricia.

Tricia has been such a support, calling me to see how I am, sending me cards to cheer me up. She was glad to hear that I have a plan, happy to hear me sounding optimistic again.

I called to cancel the second oncologist's appointment. I called Mary Lou's friend and arranged to get her book back to her. I called Burton Goldberg's office and asked them to overnight a copy of his book to me at the Institute. See how efficient? What a hard worker I am? Even when there's no one to applaud me, I'm driven.

I called Sid and asked if he'll take me to the airport. He said he'd be happy to take me to the airport but he's not too comfortable about why.

"Are you sure…are you sure this is the right thing to do?"

I told him I was sure, that it just *feels* right. I told him there was something he can do to support me and that's to visualize me old and healthy.

He was quiet for a second then said he can do that.

This afternoon I got a card in the mail from Larry, offering hugs and, he added, kisses. We've gotten together a lot in the last couple of weeks and it would be really nice to drift into a cozy relationship with him. But I think about the other woman he's not sure he's over and tell myself *forget it*. Unless it was smooth sailing (unlikely), the anxiety would cause me even more stress than I already have. I called to tell him I'm going away for a few weeks. He offered to pick me up at the airport but Sid already is so we agreed to watch the sunset together the day after I get back.

* * *

Friday. Halloween's one of my favorite holidays here and a part of me really wants to join the crowd in Waikiki tonight. I love seeing people be so creative. And it's fun to watch the Japanese tourists have such fun. They'll take pictures of *anything* (like the dinner cruise I was on where my Japanese table mate videoed his wife eating) and on Halloween they're excited to actually have *interesting* things to take pictures of. For the last couple of years the guys from the gay bar have come out (ha, pun) around 11 p.m., swaggering on spiky heels, dresses slit up to…well, way up, tossing glamour hair-dos more seductively than I ever could.

I love watching the fun that people have but I probably need rest for the flight tomorrow more, so I'm staying home.

* * *

November, 1997

Saturday morning. I scrambled around yesterday to get all the loose ends tied up before I leave and I guess I over-performed because now I don't have a thing to do till the plane leaves this afternoon. I wish I were going for a simple cure. Well, maybe I am. The doctors here only think about fighting the disease, at any cost. I feel that it's important for my body to be well. The Institute is the first step and I'll decide what to do next later.

Even though I'll have Goldberg's book, I'm on my way to a place that will help me detoxify and I'm on Dr. Pfeil's waiting list, I still worry. What if this isn't the right thing to do? Sometimes it would be *so* easy to give in, to go along with what the doctors want me to do. Insurance would pay. I'd be off work, away from Gunther.

But I know I'd also be falling into a behavior pattern I've brought from childhood: fight some then, after a certain amount of resistance from others, give up, give in, and be a victim. The stakes are higher now, though. This isn't about an argument or a job. This is about my life.

I tried to read but can't concentrate. I'm glad I'm going to the Institute, so why am I starting to feel anxious about leaving Hawaii? Hawaii is where my soul is, yet I have the oddest fear that I might not be coming back. But unless the plane crashes or I die at the Institute (neither is likely), I'll be back in three weeks. I'll have a cleaner body and I'll have more information. Why isn't there a health institute on one of the neighbor islands?

Saturday night. I'm in San Diego. Sid brought me a red ginger going-away lei and on the ride to the airport the fragrance filled the cab of his truck; that, and an uncomfortable silence. Neither of us could find anything to say that we hadn't already said. He dropped me off at the curb and his hug felt detached. As I walked the long corridor to the departure gate I listened to the Hawaiian music, noticed the feeling of the tropical breeze on my skin; is this one of the last trips I'll ever make?

The flight was uneventful and I listened to the first three Caroline Myss tapes. It's clear to me already that Caroline wouldn't put up with Gunther for a minute. She's funny, spiritual, and tough. No nonsense. It's an interesting combination and I need to ponder that someone can be spiritual and not necessarily be compelled to be nice all the time! I'm funny, I'm spiritual, but I've always felt that being spiritual means I have to be nice so I've become unwilling to stand up to anyone if I think it might lead to hurt feelings or conflict.

There was too much conflict when I was growing up and I don't like the way it feels. I don't like what it does to relationships. I've learned to discuss issues calmly, isn't that a good thing?

Okay, I don't try to discuss issues with some people calmly because I let things go beyond the place where I can still be calm talking about them and I don't challenge some people because I'm pretty sure I wouldn't win. Why is winning so important? It's not enough to just say what I need to say but I have to win or else I feel that they've gotten some control over me. Am I still trying to win arguments with my parents?

Sherry offered to loan me her Myss tapes, I wonder if they'll be the same ones Mary Lou loaned me. What are the chances that my dietitian and my sister-in-law would both be fans of a medical intuitive – a subject I'm guaranteed to be interested in? Synchronicity again.

After five hours wedged between a wall and a stranger, we landed at LAX. Fifteen minutes on the shuttle to the car rental barn, another ten in line behind a dozen other tired travelers, and I was on my way.

I spent dozens of years driving L.A. freeways and knew the two-hour drive to San Diego would be boring so to entertain myself I thought about home. On Oahu I can drive around the island in less than three hours. I go over the Pali Highway, cutting through lush rain forests and mountain tops where the wind can literally knock over a small child.

If I take the long way, I go through Kailua town, turn left at the T and follow the tree-lined road past the access road to Kaneohe Marine Base and the bay. I wind left to Kaneohe town, then in about 15 minutes the road winds left again at Kualoa Ranch and hugs the dazzling blue ocean through Kahaluu, Waiahole, Kaaawa, Punaluu, and Hauula. Old houses, modest ones built before Hawaii was so expensive, nest on the sandy beach. A lot of the houses on the opposite side of the street are on supports to keep them dry in case of flood. After a dozen or so houses the beach is empty again for miles and the water changes shades from perfectly clear to turquoise to sea green and back.

Just after Laie (and the Polynesian Cultural Center) I usually stop at Giovani's Shrimp Truck for a half order of shrimp and rice buried in garlic. At Kahuku, Kamehameha Highway turns inland till Kawela Bay, then I pass Sunset Beach and Waimea Bay. Sometimes I catch a glimpse of surf tournaments as I drive by. A couple of times I've stopped to watch but if the waves aren't good it's kind of boring.

Most of the time I stop in Haleiwa, get some ice cream and wander the shops, then head back home. Once in awhile, though, I take the road that goes farther north, out past Mokuleia Beach Park, past the skydiving airport, past the tiny airport where people go for glider rides. But the road ends without completing the loop to Waianae so I head back on the old highway and catch the freeway to town. Every time I make that drive I think, *thank God I get to live in Hawaii.*

On the drive to San Diego I passed mostly drab buildings and when I did pass the ocean it was too dark to see. People drive scary fast here! Trucks are so huge!

It was 9:11 p.m. when I pulled into Julie's driveway. The fall air felt cold against my skin. My breath felt cold in my lungs. It's been three years since I've felt chilly, winter air.

Julie's house is gorgeous, of course. Her houses are always gorgeous. We stayed up late talking about old writing friends, books, and, of course, cancer, then finally went to bed. It feels odd to feel a cold floor under my feet and a cold toilet seat under my okole.

* * *

Sunday. Julie invited me to come back after I leave the Institute and stay for as long as I like. I appreciate her offer but Hawaii is already pulling at me and I know that after the health farm I'll need to be home.

About 2 p.m. we went to return my rental car, then off to the Institute. I hadn't given any thought to what the place would look like, I'd only focused on what went on there and suddenly I started wondering what I'd gotten myself into. But when we pulled into the parking lot I was relieved to see a sprawling group of pleasant looking one- and two-story buildings, white, around a grassy lawn. A couple dozen people sprawled on lawn furniture; I can almost pretend I'm here on vacation.

Most of the complex is on the main level and is shaped like an arch: the lobby is front left, then a large room where we'll eat and have lectures. On the "top" of the arch is the swimming pool, and beyond that is a huge nursery where they grow wheat grass. On the right side are more guest rooms. Outside the arch on the right there's a small gift shop and on the lower level there's a chapel, a library, more guest rooms, and on the left a room with refrigerators and sinks that hold fresh-cut wheat grass and several dozen juicing machines. Next to it there's a spa where we can get massages. Way down the hill there's a laundry room and more parking.

By the time I got to my room my luggage was there. I hung up my shirts, folded my jeans in a drawer, lined up the 15 books about cancer I'd brought then went back to the lobby to mingle.

It was late afternoon and I was starving so one of the staff brought me a leftover lunch salad of raw squash and sprouts. I wolfed it down and a few hours later I was doubled over on the floor trying to remember to breath through the pains that ripped through my belly.

Not used to such dense, raw food, the staff said. Not used to much food at all, actually. I've barely eaten in the last two weeks because I don't know what I should be eating.

I listened to the welcome talk in the fetal position on the floor, trying to relax and breathe. There was a second talk scheduled for later and I planned to go but I needed a short nap first. I woke up a few hours later feeling a little better but there was no way I was leaving my bed.

* * *

Monday. Day 2. There's a morning routine we're encouraged to follow, starting with exercise. Ugh. First we stretch, then we go for a long walk into some vacant land; up some hills and down. Then we stretch again. I don't like to exercise and I'm weak from not eating but I did my best.

After the second round of stretching we queued up for breakfast – juice made from raw green vegetables. There was actually a choice between green vegetable juice and delicious-looking watermelon slices but the staff said anyone who needs to avoid sugar should choose the green juice so I did. I told myself it wasn't really a choice between green juice and watermelon; it was a choice between green juice and chemo.

I hate that I'm weak and self-indulgent with food (except for lately), and that I usually have zero will power to say no to sugar. Why? I can be feeling ill from having too many cookies and still eat more. I can tell myself, okay, only one more. Well, two. I keep saying that even after six or seven more. When I feel really uncomfortable, I try to hold on to the sensation so I can remember it next time I'm around sugar but I never do.

At the morning welcoming session we were told that the gift shop carries most of the products we'll need that we might not have brought along and specifically, we were told to be sure to purchase enema kits. Everybody groaned.

We were also told we might want to check out colonics and were given the name and address of a woman in town who does them. What in the world makes someone choose that as their career? I can't imagine going back to a high school reunion!

A couple times a day we're supposed to juice enough wheat grass for a four-ounce glass. Oh, yeah, and drink it. We're also supposed to drink something called Rejuvelac as many times a day as possible. It's supposed to be super nutritious and we get to choose fermented wheat or rye and it tastes like…ummm…maybe the vinegar-water rag they wipe a bar off with?

Before and after lunch there are lectures about different kinds of illness, how food affects health, why exercise is so important, how what we think contributes to our health.

I remember in the fourth or fifth grade seeing a chart about the food groups in a balanced diet and thinking, boy, I'm going to have trouble keeping this straight. Weird, huh? I've used my bad eating habits as a time- and money-saver, and as a conversation piece. No more. I'm still not sure what a healthy anti-cancer diet is, but I intend to find out and follow it.

The staff tell us about all the amazing things that have happened here and they show slides of former guests coming in with a lump on their neck or arm or forehead and leaving without it.

Staff always adds that they can't claim the person was healed, but we can all see the photos: Before the Institute, lump. After the Institute, no lump. Several of the guests shared stories about friends of theirs who've been "cured." I wonder if I could get well just with this program. I think, maybe, but a deeper part of me says no, this will help but I need something else, too. I'm reading Goldberg's book and am counting on Dr. Pfeil.

Everybody seems really nice. Most of us took our lunch out onto the grass and it felt very healing to be in the warm sun.

* * *

Tuesday. Day 3. I am *hungry*. Before I got the cancer verdict I weighed 133 lbs. Now I'm 121. I think this must be what starving people feel like and sometimes I resent the staff – I go into my victim mode and think they could make the food more palatable if they wanted to. Other times I feel a little proud of myself for doing this when it is so hard.

The routine is getting easier but I'm lusting after some of my old food. I hope, the Institute hopes, that once I get used to a regular diet of healthy food my craving for bad foods will go away.

During the lectures I lie on the floor at the back of the room listening with one part of my brain while I read and highlight relevant material in Goldberg's book with another. It's my plan to read through the entire 1,100+ pages while I'm here, quickly, not really processing the information but highlighting what applies to me. I'm marking the protocols that most of the doctors have in common and then will look at including them in my wellness plan when I get home.

I'm *really* impressed with the book. The doctors have good success rates and impressive credentials and it gives me hope that I can be well without doing anything drastic. The first doctor lives in New York, got his degree from Cornell University Medical College, won the National Health Federation Man of the Year award in 1985, won the World Organization of Alternative Medicine Recognition of Achievement in 1990, hosts two health-oriented radio talk shows and has written a bunch of books.

The second is Keith I. Block, M.D., the past medical director of the Cancer Institute at Edgewater Medical Center in Chicago and [at press time] the Medical and Scientific Director of the Block Center for Integrative Medicine, the editor-in-chief for a peer-reviewed cancer journal, *Integrative Cancer Therapies* published by Sage Science Press, and a Clinical Assistant Professor at the University of Illinois College of Medicine in Chicago.

Several of the doctors in the book have been oncologists. One doctor in Nevada has been an associate professor of medicine at the University of Nevada at Reno and has served as chief of oncology at Washoe Medical Center and Sparks Family Hospital, both in Reno.

A doctor in Florida has been clinical assistant professor in the Department of Radiation Oncology at the University of Miami School of Medicine and was in practice as a radiation oncologist at Baptist Hospital in Miami. Another New York doctor received the American Medical Association's Physician's Recognition Award in Continuing Medical Education and has written several books.

A doctor in New Jersey was trained in oncology and clinical immunology and worked at the National Cancer Institute as a clinical associate in the immunology branch, then as investigator in the pharmacology branch. I feel like they know what they're talking about and I'm very grateful to have been led to this book.

I think about moving, temporarily, to be able to work with one of them. I could stay with relatives…. But I think I'd have to have a lot more money than I have and I'd need to be more convinced that I actually do still have cancer to be willing to do that.

Yesterday we had a cancer slide show so now I know exactly what those buggers look like and I can visualize them turning into vapor and floating far, far away.

Later. The words still haunt me. Maybe *it's time to go* means it's time to go from my old life of stress and junk food to one where I manage stress, eat well and have lots of fun. I like that idea. I live in one of the most beautiful places in the world and I have great friends. I love my daughter dearly and feel blessed that she loves me the same way. Why would I leave?

Tonight a psychologist came to give a talk and to demonstrate a problem-solving technique. You sit in a chair and put your problem in a chair facing you and then you talk to the problem, tell it what's on your mind, ask questions. After you've said it all you go sit in the other chair and answer as the problem.

The doc asked for volunteers and there's something that's keeping me at a low but constant level of panic. The idea absolutely terrifies me. My hand shot up and he invited me to sit in the first chair.

"I'm afraid," I said to the empty chair where the "problem" sat, "now that I have a pre-existing medical condition…I'm afraid I'll have to stay at my terrible job forever just to have health insurance."

The doctor waited for me to go on, but that was all.

"Okay," he said, "go sit in the problem's chair and respond as the problem."

"Why are you worrying?" the problem asked, "with no information at all? You haven't made one phone call to see if what you're afraid of is correct."

Wow. I was amazed! The answer had just sprung from my mouth and I knew immediately that it was so true! So far the problem only exists in my mind. I feel like I've just taken off a 30-pound jacket I've been lugging around for weeks.

* * *

Wednesday. Day 4. Mary Lou told me she knew a doctor at the Institute I should talk to while I'm here so this morning I found him and introduced myself. I asked what he knows about alternative care and what he thinks he'd do in my situation. Les showed me brochures from two places, one in Mexico (the same one Rebecca had told me about) and one in San Diego that's run by a man who isn't a doctor, but who used to be with one of the Mexico clinics. Les said he can't endorse either, I need to investigate on my own.

Our group, the people here this week, are a nice bunch. Mostly women. One heartbreaker though – a youngish, not highly educated woman is here with her daughter. Mary has just had a mastectomy and she doesn't bother to even put a sock in her empty bra cup so her shirts hang sadly. Mary doesn't seem to notice. She's got more worrying things on her mind. She's a single parent, her daughter's about 11, and she's afraid of what will happen to her daughter if she doesn't survive. It's clear they both adore each other. The love between the two is so obvious it makes my heart ache to think what she must be feeling.

We're kept busy but we also have time to ourselves and I'm doing a lot of thinking. I know there are people who think that disease just happens and I guess sometimes that's true. I think of babies, and perfect people who meditate and exercise and always choose fruit for dessert and can limit themselves to only one scoop of Bubbies Double Chocolate Chocolate Chip Ice Cream.

But I feel that my cancer happened as a direct result of what I have and haven't been doing. I've weakened my immune system with years of overly stressful jobs and constant stress. I've put sugar and fatty food into my body and expected it to function. I've given my body cheap food that has little nutrition though I'd never dream of putting iced tea in my car just because it's cheaper than gas. It seems like I don't value myself very much.

Later. I am just about sick of green food. The last few meals have at least been things we can chew, but still green and with about as much flavor as Easter basket grass. When I booked my stay here the reservation clerk told me not to bring any food or snacks, no seasonings, nada. Rebecca told me to forget what they say, to bring seasoning. I didn't. Now I wish I had. I did bring my little bottle of liquid oxygen and take hits from it in my room like a closet alcoholic. Except it doesn't taste very good.

Curt called to say that there was a law passed fairly recently that requires workplace insurance companies to cover everything. They can't exclude pre-existing conditions! So I can change jobs without having to worry. What a relief! What would it take for me to remember not to worry about things until I actually have to?

Curt's going to try to come down from Irvine on Sunday – I hope he can. I loved having him as my best friend when I lived in Newport Beach and it's been too long since we've seen each other.

This afternoon I called the clinics in Mexico and

San Diego and they're going to send me brochures. I'm pretty sure I won't go to Mexico but there's no harm in learning more.

Most of the time when I'm in my room I listen to the Caroline Myss tapes and I love them. She's funny and very smart and she reminds me of things I already know but forget. Example: The things I think and say and do create what happens in my life. That's why I shouldn't focus on what makes me angry or afraid.

Mary and her daughter are so sweet. Mary gave me a little gold-colored pin for friendship and I wear it on my shirt. I wish I could let myself connect with her in the way I feel she wants me to, but I can't. The ego part of me wants to hang out with people who have similar energy and interests. Or maybe I just need to be with people whose problems don't seem worse than my own.

In the first orientation talk one of the staff suggested we buy a natural bristle brush (available in the gift shop) and dry brush our skin. She said if we do that every day before we shower, we'll slough off enough dead skin that we can lose two pounds of toxins by the time we leave. One of Goldberg's doctors also recommends dry brushing. Says it helps remove flakes of dead skin that may contain toxins and that it also stimulates the circulation of lymph and blood to the skin. I like it whenever I read that one of the doctors recommends doing something we're doing here. Sort of lends credibility to both.

Several of the doctors in Goldberg's book recommend qigong or Tai Chi and I promise to look into one or the other when I get back home. I actually still have the green belt I got in karate when I was in my 20s. If I'd stayed in martial arts would I be battling cancer? Probably not. I'd have gotten plenty of exercise to oxygenate my blood so those cancer cells couldn't stay. But it's no good second-guessing. Maybe I'd have gotten kicked in the head and died 10 years ago.

Several of the docs in Goldberg's book think it's important to detox so I'm glad I'm here. Most of the doctors recommend varying dosages of vitamins A, B, C and E; several recommend shark cartilage, Essiac tea, beta carotene, selenium and coenzyme Q10 (also called CoQ10). I've already got the tea, I'll check the other stuff out when I get back home. Another project.

A lot of the lectures here are about food and nutrition. It makes sense (and of course I must have known it) that the body will work better with proper fuel. But bad food is everywhere! Except, of course, here. I think about Walter, an older guy I worked with once. He had a triple bypass heart surgery and was off work for weeks. When he came back he brought Swanson's frozen fried chicken dinners every day for lunch. I asked him if that was a good thing for him to be eating, considering what he'd just been through, and he said, "The doctor didn't say I couldn't," and kept on bringing them.

We've been discouraged from leaving campus but I needed a notebook to write in and a change of scenery so this afternoon I walked six blocks to Thrifty Drugs. It felt good to be outside in a different neighborhood. I'm not used to being limited to one place for days in a row.

The weather is nice, mid-seventies and I paced my newly weakened self so I wouldn't get tired. It's really strange how quickly you get acclimated to a new place and how quickly old experiences fade. I've been at the Institute for nearly a week, haven't gone into a store except the small gift shop. Thrifty's felt strange and huge. It smelled different, sounded different, and before I'd taken six steps inside I was literally overwhelmed by the number and size of the displays of junk food. Mountains of chips. Towers of soda. Rows after perfect rows of candy in brightly colored choose-me wrappers. I ducked my head to block it all out, grabbed a notebook and left fast as I could.

After my walk I decided to sprawl in the sun before dinner. Steve plunked himself down in the chair next to mine and I asked him why he lives here. He said it's temporary, he trades handyman skills for room and board. He told me, seemed to make a point of telling me, that he doesn't get involved with women guests unless they give him a clear sign that they want him to. I hope he isn't hinting to me because I have no interest.

Some of the people who are here have cancer but most don't. Some don't have anything wrong at all, they just come here for the juice diet to flush out their systems. One or two come every year. They say they just eat whatever they want all year, then come here to flush it out and start over. I'm grateful for what I think this is going to do for me but I sure wouldn't choose to spend time here on vacation!

Yea. At lunch they announced that on Friday we get applesauce. It's mind boggling how much we're all looking forward to such a little thing as unsweetened mashed apples.

Stress lecture this afternoon. Stress seems to be a way of life these days but it's getting blamed for a lot of cancers. I know when I'm stressed and I probably know a thousand ways to reduce stress but I'm always too busy to do any of them. I know I should have done last year differently. When should I have left my job? Actually, I shouldn't have taken the job in the first place. I didn't like the feel of the building, didn't like the energy of the place from the minute I walked in the door. I didn't like the way the owner behaved when we met.... So many warning signs but I kept telling myself I was just being judgmental, that sometimes I had to put up with things I didn't like.

My body had longed for me to run out and down the stairs the first day and never go back and I *wanted* to but I was too embarrassed – how could I explain it to the owner? What would I do to pay the rent?

I stayed because I had a strong belief that I was in that job because there was something I needed to learn and if I didn't learn it there I'd just replicate a bad situation at my next job. I told that to someone here and he said, "Maybe what you needed to learn was to get out of a situation you hated!" Duh. Why didn't *I* think of that?

* * *

Thursday. Day 5. Last night I woke up from a deep sleep with a dream message. I knew it was important: "You can do this, but not alone." I believe it was a confirmation that I'm on the right path and this morning I called Dr. Pfeil's receptionist again to see how I'm progressing on the waiting list. She promises me that once I'm home she'll be able to squeeze me in to see him.

For the last few days we've been having raw vegetable salads for lunch and dinner. Not enough flavor for me to want to eat it. Actually, not enough flavor to be *able* to eat it. There's something natural they sell in the gift shop that spices up food some. They mean for us to take it home, but I bought some to use here and sometimes I bring my food back to my room and sprinkle some over it. I feel like a junkie hiding her stash. But I've got to stop losing weight.

We just had a lecture about food combining. I've done it before and plan on doing it again when I get home. Basically, the concept is that proteins and carbohydrates don't digest at the same rate and if you eat them at the same time not all your food gets digested and whatever doesn't get digested just hangs around. Your immune system gets so bogged down trying to clean out the garbage that it doesn't have time to get around to other things, like cancer cells.

With food combining, you eat either carbs or protein and wait at least two hours before eating the other. One other thing about food combining is that it will force me to be very conscious of everything I eat.

They also talk about being vegan (no animal or dairy products) and Dr. Keith Block says that a person on a mainly vegan diet tends to repel cancer far more successfully than someone on a high-fat diet. He says his research shows that vegans have 2.5 times the cancer-killing potential as omnivores. I haven't eaten meat in a couple of years, I stopped eating chicken and turkey years ago because they started making me urpy. I don't think I eat a *lot* of cheese, hardly ever have an egg. I can stop completely for a while.

* * *

Friday. Day 6. In the shower this morning I thought I felt a lump at the edge of my breast and instantly felt that grungy dread wash through my body. I don't want it to be more cancer. Isn't it too soon? I know there are lumps in my breast that are okay but how do I know which is which? I got a massage at the spa downstairs and I asked the manager to check it to see what she thought. Thank goodness, she said she didn't feel anything to worry about. I pray God she's right. I feel like I'm walking a brave path but sometimes I don't feel brave at all. Scary thoughts leap out at me and even though they can't kill me I know the cancer can. Could. If I still had it. Which I don't.

Most of the time I can be positive that I'm doing the right thing but still, sometimes I'm powerfully afraid.

I spent an hour sitting in the sun listening to Caroline Myss tapes. She talks about the way we leak our energy and I know my energy is leaking, going someplace instead of staying with me.

God knows I need it all with me right now, so I've come up with a plan to help me change gears: Whenever I catch myself thinking angry or scary thoughts I'm going to interrupt myself with a mental picture of a TV journalist pushing a microphone toward me and saying, "So tell me, Karin Ireland, have you always known you'd be rich and famous?" I will modestly admit that I have and then start telling them about my latest best-selling book. Zing, my energy is right back with me and I'm thinking about something I'd like to have happen instead of something I wouldn't.

Caroline's very funny. Her humor's good for me because it makes me laugh. Also, I see her as a highly spiritual person and yet she says exactly what's on her mind. I'm sure she edits some, but still....

Finally, tonight we had...ta da...real food! After *way* too many green vegetable meals I had applesauce – an amazing combination of sweet and tart tastes – and special unbaked crackers for dinner and they were absolutely WONDERFUL!

We also had a fun variety show. On Wednesday Sandy asked for volunteers to emcee the program and I actually wanted to do it but I hesitated too long before raising my hand and someone else offered. I volunteered to clog dance at the show, though, and for some reason I brought some bluegrass tapes with me!

The dance went well, considering that I was trying to chug my stockinged feet on the carpet. Several people came up to congratulate me afterwards. I was puzzled, though. Since there were about 15 rows of chairs I asked if they could see my feet. No, they said, they couldn't. Then what did they like??? Clogging is all about feet!

Steve played the didgeridoo, which I didn't know is a vibrational healing instrument. Mary played the piano while her daughter played violin. I hope Mary will survive.

* * *

Saturday. Day 7. Today I'm actually feeling pretty peppy. I took a long walk uphill and I have more energy than when I started. I called Larry and left a teaser message on his machine about romantic sunsets when I get back.

In Goldberg's book, Dr. Keith Block starts with the least invasive treatment and moves to more invasive therapies, *only* if it's clear that they're needed and, even then, *only* with the patient's input. Right after someone's diagnosed he offers *days* of special education so his patients can learn about the options, about diet, exercise, stress management, etc. He's in Evanston, Illinois, I have relatives in Oklahoma....

He says what I believe, I guess what *everybody* believes – that chemotherapy, radiation and surgery are hard on the body, depress immunity, poison the body. The difference is that he's willing to use less invasive therapies first.

He writes about a woman with breast cancer who'd eaten high-fat foods all her life (like me) and had had surgery and chemo. Three years later it came back, metastasizing to her bones. Several specialists said there wasn't anything they could do and that she had maybe a year to live. She went to Dr. Block and now she's fine and it's 13 years after the other doctors said she had a year to live. Why doesn't the medical community look at this man and learn from him? Dr. Martin said she wished she had another way to tell me about. Dr. Block's got another way. I'll loan her my book when I get back. Maybe this is what she needs to get her to explore some.

At lunch I looked from my fork to my bony arm. I really like my belly being so flat but I need more weight (up today to 119) on my arms and legs. I tell myself I need to eat more and I try, but it's hard. Everything is so bland. Now there's a diet idea, create a pill that blocks a person's taste buds. Dang, I could be a gazillionaire.

We did validating tonight, the exercise where people say what they feel about you. I've done it before and it always amazes me that people who have only talked to you once or twice can still pick up on the essence of who you are. My ego loves that when it was my turn to be validated 10 people put their hands up immediately to volunteer. The three people who talked about me said really lovely things. I like this sense of community here and I wish I could find a group of people to be friends with at home.

When I get back I'm going to look for ways to bring more people into my life. I realize I've been a loner for years. I go out to dance, but other than that I seem to choose to stay home and write. I'm a social person, I need to be with people more than I am. Years ago I had a yellow Post-it on my computer monitor that said BALANCE to help me remember to have balance in my life. It's so easy to say, *I'll work at being balanced after I finish this book.* But then the next book is in my mind and I forget.

* * *

Sunday. Day 8. Today Curt drove down from Irvine for lunch. We haven't seen each other for too long. The Institute will pack lunches for us if we're going off campus so I took a green salad (surprise) and we went to a restaurant. Lots of tempting food but all I ordered was a side of avocado. I appreciate Curt for being the first person to tell me I'm smart. I was in my late 40s and I hadn't believed him at first, but he'd kept telling me that he'd never been able to have conversations with anyone who had the range of knowledge I did, who was as sharp and fast a thinker.... How had I gotten to middle age believing I was "less than" almost everybody else. Where did I get that picture of myself? From my parents (I never did anything right), school (lack of interest led to lack of information and poor grades). Even when I've had jobs where everybody thought I was great and told me so I believed I was good at the job but it didn't translate to being smart. Sigh.

* * *

Monday. Day 9. On Saturday a lot of people went home and yesterday a bunch of new people came. They don't seem nearly as much fun. To be fair, it's rainy and no one sits outside so we don't have a chance to get to know each other. Some people hang out in the lobby and in the rec room, but it's not the same energy at all.

Two of the new ladies come to meals drenched in perfume, even though the brochures ask guests please not to use any because a lot of people feel nauseated on this diet. It smelled really unpleasant and I wish I had the nerve to say something, but I don't. I hear my mother's voice, and I can't give myself permission to ask someone to change just because it's what *I* want. Experiences like this remind me that I'm willing to put up with a lot in order to avoid conflict or to avoid feeling guilty about saying something that someone who's nice wouldn't say.

As a kid, I fought with my parents constantly and of course they always told me it was my fault. All my arguing never made a difference; all it did was make us all angry and estranged. I tell myself I'm a spiritual person now and I don't need to let myself get drawn into confrontations. I tell myself that I should be able to just accept that Gunther does what he does and these women wear perfume and I can just ignore them all. I tell myself that, but clearly, I can't.

At lunch a seriously large lady (300+ pounds, I'd guess) arrived in a wheelchair. Although no one asked, she announced somewhat angrily that she's not here to lose weight. Whatever.

Tonight the sunset was gorgeous. I love Hawaii sunsets and forget how a smog-filled California horizon can make the yellow sun turn a beautiful orangey red.

* * *

Tuesday. Day 10. Today was rainy again and the heaters went out in my building so I took a book to the lounge area and read, restlessly. This week there are five of us here from Hawaii! Three from Oahu and two from the Big Island. Why do we have to come to California to get well? There should be a huge wellness retreat on the Big Island where people from all around the world can come to do this kind of cleansing and healing. There's lots of room there, land's not as expensive as on Oahu, it's beautiful, there are fancy hotels for the rest of the family to stay in. Plus, the land has a wonderful, healing energy.

Tricia and I talk on the phone every couple of days and she is such a comfort to me. This morning she called and she's sick. She's going to fly down for a day while I'm at Art's, so I hope she can get well quick.

I'm doing pretty well drinking a lot of the water, I'm juicing wheat grass once a day, but I'm not drinking the Rejuvelac much at all. And if my survival hangs on doing the enemas, then I might as well just order a coffin today. I'm not doing it. Does that say something about my willpower? I prefer to think that I intuitively know what will help and what isn't that important and I'm doing what's important (eating green stuff vs. watermelon).

* * *

Wednesday. Day 11. Hump day. Kerri called from the office with news – Gunther has gone out on disability because of – stress!!!!! Is he nuts? How can he go out on stress? He *is* the stress. I think I need to do a lot of anger clearing about him.

I'm still listening to the Caroline Myss tapes several times a day. They remind me to be mindful of what I think about, to have a clear intent about what I want to create. I already know all that, it's just that after a while I get overwhelmed.

Caroline talks about being conscious of how you spend your energy and says imagine you get 100 credits of energy each day. If you spend 30 credits thinking about your jerky old boss and 20 worrying about where you're going to work next and 40 feeling sorry for yourself about some wrong somebody did to you – you've only got 10 credits left to manage/create your whole day! What can you accomplish that's good when you're spending so much of it on things that are *not* good for you?

I need to let Gunther go. He's an ass, everybody agrees he is, so I don't need to spend any more time going over it in my head. I don't need to worry about a job – I'm hoping I won't have to go back to my old job but that's not something I have to deal with right now. I'll trust that I'll have what I need when I need it. I might as well spend my 100 energy credits thinking about how healthy I'm becoming, about how to shop for and cook foods that are good for me.

I went to the movies tonight with two other women from here. My mouth watered remembering the taste of salted buttery hot popped corn.... I could feel the Coke fizzing down my throat.... We walked past the concession counter, eyes forward, without slowing down. The three of us were the only ones in the theatre and we sat and sat and sat...ten minutes after it was supposed to start Jacklyn went out to ask someone to turn the movie on. She says she also told the manager that her time was valuable and that she didn't appreciate that they didn't care enough to start on time, etc., and the manager offered us all popcorn and a drink! She told him no, we couldn't eat it, so he gave us free passes to come back.

I marvel at her. Was it confidence or pushiness that let her say what she did to the manager? Maybe she just knows she can get away with saying whatever's on her mind and she gets away with it because of her attitude. She's funny, so I suspect she says things with a touch of humor...a nice skill to develop, I think.

Is it better to speak up or to decide not to let things bother you? I keep going 'round and 'round with this. I've been taught it's better to detach and just let things slide on past but I also understand it's good to speak up. Bernie Siegel says the "good girl who tries to please and internalizes anger" is the profile of a cancer patient.

Maybe the decider is whether you actually *can* let things not bother you or whether you just pretend and then stuff the anger. Like me. I'd try to tell myself just to ignore Gunther but I couldn't and then I'd get angry with myself for letting it bother me. I didn't speak up to the owner at all, and she's the one who could have made a difference. Why didn't I? I try to play by the rules and you're not supposed to go over your boss's head and besides, I didn't think she would do anything. But how do I know unless I try?

Okay, that's the goal, I think, to get where I let things go when I can, speak up when I can't, and am ready to walk in case it doesn't look like things are going to change. I need to work on letting go of my attachments to how I think I have to behave and look for ways to take care of myself. Tomorrow night I'm going dancing! Ta da! Catherine, one of the staff here, goes to Denim and Diamonds every week and she offered to give me a ride. Then one more day and I'm off to Art's for a few days and to see Tricia.

* * *

Thursday. Day 12. This week the Institute is offering classes to teach us how to eat only raw food once we get back home. How to make cookies and bread without cooking. A great idea but I know me; it's not gonna happen. How to dehydrate fruits and vegetables. Ditto. How to grow your own wheat grass to drink. Ditto ditto.

Tonight I went dancing in Mission Valley and tested my two-step legs and they still work. It felt wonderful. Good two-step music, a good partner and room to move is my idea of complete bliss. It's 11:30 and it's the latest I've stayed up the whole time I've been here.

* * *

Friday. Day 13. Tomorrow I go back to the real world. I'm glad I came here but I'm ready to go. Between Goldberg's book and the Institute, I have a new respect for food, I know what I eat matters and am willing to spend the money and time to eat food that's good for me. I've got a pretty good idea of what my diet should be. Lots of fish, raw fruits and vegetables (organic), seeds, nuts, purified water. I'll use rice or soy milk instead of dairy.

I'll avoid everything that's processed, which will automatically eliminate food additives and dyes.

One of the lectures last week was about cosmetic dyes, chemicals and preservatives and how toxic they are so I plan to go through my stuff once I get home and will probably have to throw most of it out. I'll also get rid of all my cleaning stuff that has toxic ingredients.

Goldberg's book has convinced me that there are respected doctors out there who are helping people get well without drastic treatment and it gives me confidence that I'm on the right path. Several of these docs say the first step is to flush all the toxins out of the body and so I'm glad I've come here. I know I wouldn't have the will-power to stay on such a strict diet at home. The bad part is that I only weigh 113 lbs., down from 133. I'm 5'9! That's not enough!

Tonight was the variety show and Wednesday when they asked for a volunteer to be emcee I got my hand up right away. About 50 people showed up and I opened by saying that David Letterman had actually planned on being the host but due to a last-minute scheduling conflict he'd had to cancel but he did send along his 10 top reasons to stay at Optimum Health Institute. I was pretty hammy and some of it was kind of gross insider humor but I got a lot of laughs.

* * *

Saturday. Day 14. Art got here at noon. It was really good to see him and sweet of him to come get me. It makes me feel good to have my friends rallying around me, coming to visit, offering to let me stay with them. Before we left San Diego we drove down to the beach and walked around Coronado. It felt odd but good to be away from the relatively small space of the Institute. Great to see the ocean, to put my feet in the sand.

On the drive back to L.A. we stopped at an outlet mall in Lake Elsinore and I went into a kitchen store. The largest kitchen store on Oahu is about a quarter the size of this place and there isn't nearly the dazzling variety. Who knew you needed a separate vegetable scrubber for each vegetable?

A few miles from Art's house we stopped at Mrs. Gooches' health food store to get me some healthy food. I was amazed to see rows and rows of organic fruits and veggies, three times the selection and a third the cost of what's available in Hawaii.

Art's still recovering from surgery to help him stop snoring and he's in quite a bit of pain, so we're not the peppy people we might be, but when we got to his house we cleaned up and went to the Hacienda Hotel to dance a little.

* * *

Monday. Art took the day off and we drove to Balboa Island, my old stomping grounds, and wandered in and out of the shops. I'd forgotten how nice the ferry to the peninsula is – it only takes a few minutes but it's fun to watch the pelicans swoop for fish and actually dive in the water. We stayed there for dinner and went to Scott's For Fish and I had my first real dinner in a month – gently poached salmon and crunchy steamed veggies. It was heaven. Then we went to my old hangout, Cowboy Boogie, and danced.

* * *

Tuesday. I got up at the crack of dawn, literally, to take Art to work and then pick up Tricia at the airport. I always get excited waiting for the first glimpse of her and when her head poked through the crowd a feeling of love swept over me that almost left me breathless. I just *can't* die and leave her. It's been a month since my surgery, I think I'm doing the right thing.

We decided to go to Santa Monica and see the shops on Third Street Mall. We zig-zagged from one side of Third Street to the other, checking out restaurants, bookstores, clothing and music stores. It felt just like when we came here from Newport Beach to watch the perform- ers – jugglers, comedians, musicians. I think Honolulu should do this in Chinatown, close Maunakea to cars and make it a permanent walking street.

I told Tricia about the Institute and what I was learning from Caroline Myss and from Goldberg's book. I asked her if she was afraid for me and she said no, not after seeing me and hearing how I planned to get well. But she hugs me differently now. We can't take the future for granted anymore.

While she was growing up I always thought that when she finished college we'd live near each other, that we'd have these kinds of days every week or so and I miss that we won't. But I'm happy that she's happy in northern California and I feel blessed that I get to live in Hawaii. I'm thankful I got to see her, even if it was just for a day.

* * *

Wednesday. This morning, my last morning in California, Art wanted breakfast at a waffle house. Pro- cessed wheat, maple syrup, coffee. Omelets with eggs and cheese. Bacon and eggs. I told him I didn't think there'd be anything there I could eat but he said he was sure there would be. I felt like he was being inconsiderate but since I was his guest I didn't feel justified in insisting we go someplace else. I told myself it's just one meal, but I resented it and tried not to look at his plate while I picked at my tired fruit plate. Then off to the airport.

I've never felt a sense of being part of a place like I do in Hawaii and when I stepped inside the airplane and the local flight attendants welcomed me with their smiles and lilting aloha voices I was anxious to be home.

Five hours later, there was Oahu below. The plane banked and I could see the rugged coast of Waianae west,

Pearl Harbor and Waikiki below, and north, the green sloping mountains. Despite those earlier premonitions, I've made it home.

Outside the air conditioned gate area I stepped into the real Hawaii – soft, warm breezes, local music, friendly, happy people. I could never leave here for good.

Sid was parked at the curb and greeted me with a smile and an ilima lei, hundreds of tiny, fragile orange flowers spooning tightly to make a strand long enough. I love leis and just about everything else Hawaiian.

* * *

Thursday. This morning I went to Down to Earth and looked through their book of dangerous ingredients. Why are ingredients that are listed as being serious irritants still in everything? Why can they still use chemicals that are listed as carcinogenic? I made a list of the alphabet soup names to see what I have at home.

Later. Surprise! Every cosmetic, every cleaning product I own, has at least one of the dangerous chemicals I copied onto my list. I tossed everything – shampoos, rinses, moisturizers, lotions, make-ups, rouge, eye stuff, shower cleaners – into a large shopping bag and dumped it in the trash.

I went back to Down to Earth and spent a fortune replacing everything. Didn't know that some companies use spiders (!) in their natural cosmetics (for color, ugh).

My 'fridge' was already empty, so there hadn't been much to toss there. I bought soy cheese, soy milk, soy yogurt, organic fruits and veggies…. Instead of wheat things I got bread, crackers and pasta made with rice and spelt. I'm trying to think of this as an adventure.

I've promised myself no sugar. NO sugar. NO SUGAR. That means no candy, no ice cream, no cookies, no cake, no pudding, no pie, no brownies, no sherbet, no muffins, no cobblers, no sodas, no shakes…. I'm granting myself one exception, though: I can have one candy bar a month, but only after the 20th. I'm serious about this and I think that since the stakes are so high I can do it. Caroline talks about people who keep doing what they know will kill them and I don't want to be one of those people. If I die, it's not going to be because I couldn't say no to a cookie.

I've read that if you can stay off sugar for a month or two your craving will somehow disappear. Those writers lie. I'm dreaming about buffet tables full of desserts. But I get cheated 'cause I always wake up before I get to eat anything. The only way I can avoid sugar is to not put myself anywhere near it. It's hard but, I remind myself, not as hard as a round of chemo.

Once, in my Suzy Homemaker days, I baked a batch of cookies and they were so good I couldn't stop eating them. I started feeling sick, but I kept on eating. Finally I stood on the front porch and tossed them like Frisbees into the street. Lots of times I made cookie batter and ate it without ever bothering to make cookies. It disgusts me that I've had so little self-control. But it's different now.

I'm also giving up caffeine. No coffee. Not even decaf. No Cokes, not even diet ones. Tea? Make that herbal no caffeine, please. Instead, I've filled the bottom shelf of my refrigerator with bottles of purified water and orange naturally flavored soda water.

Tonight Larry took me to a beach in town I didn't know about to watch the sunset. He's so sweet, he brought beach chairs to sit in and a jacket for me in case I got cold. Afterward we went to Coconut Willy's to dance some. It feels good to have someone hold me and I need to keep reminding myself that he may still not be over the woman before me.

* * *

Friday. Sherry's set of Caroline Myss tapes were waiting for me when I got home from the Institute and they're different from the ones Mary Lou loaned me so I'm listening to them now. I love them as much as the first bunch!

One of the downsides to drinking lots of water is that I have to get up every night to pee. I try to stumble into the bathroom without waking up any more than I absolutely have to and this morning I got an unpleasant surprise – there was a large centipede right in the middle of the bathroom floor! Was it there all night? Did I almost step on it?

The downside to a ground-floor apartment and a bedroom with a sliding glass door that opens to a small yard is that bugs seem to be able to just walk on in. The Boric Acid I sprinkle over the threshold doesn't seem to stop them. Fortunately, cockroaches and centipedes respond well to a sharp smack with a flyswatter. I bought a string of plastic fish lights to hang around the medicine cabinet so there'll be light in there for my nightly treks.

* * *

Saturday. This morning I drove out into the country to start Misha's Reiki class like I promised. I listened to Caroline Myss tapes the whole way. She says, "Call back your power...focus on what you want instead of what you're afraid of...don't put your energy and attention in people and places that aren't good for you...." I'm working very hard to be very careful about what I think and say. It's scary that I used to say I'd like to weigh 126 lbs. or less, wished I had a flat belly and wondered about a tummy tuck. I wished I didn't have to work but could just stay home and read, and I wished Tricia and I lived closer to each other.

Well, since I'm not eating junk I weigh less than 126, and if I'd had the mastectomy I'd have qualified for a tummy tuck, free, as part of the reconstruction process. I am staying home reading – how to survive cancer, not the subject I'd have chosen – and Tricia offered to come stay with me to help me through chemo. Who was it warned us to be careful what we wish for?

After a couple hours in class we took a break and one of the women told me she'd had breast cancer and had gone through radiation therapy without any side effects. She was convinced it was because she'd gone to weekly energy balancing sessions with Master Wong in Honolulu, who does qigong.

"You should go to him," she said. "Don't tell him about your cancer. Let him do the energy balancing and afterward ask him what he found." Maybe I will.

Class ended at 5 o'clock and most everybody is going to stay the night but I'd rather sleep in my own bed and drive back. Misha warned us to expect to feel some effects of the Reiki attunement – nausea, different emotions, headaches – but I don't.

* * *

Monday. Yesterday was uneventful. Just more Reiki stuff. Today I called Master Wong for an appointment.

* * *

Wednesday. Thanksgiving Eve. This morning I lay on Master Wong's massage table while he poked and prodded some and waved his hands this way and that.

After the session he asked me in a thick Chinese accent why I'd come.

I told him I'd had a cancer lump removed six weeks ago and I wanted to know if it was all gone. "There is no cancer," he said. "He'd know if there was anything there," said Kathy, his Caucasian girlfriend. I felt relieved to hear that. As much as I want to believe I'm fine, I still worry sometimes. He said my tummy wasn't happy though and said I needed to eat more enjoyable food. I told him what I enjoy are Butterfingers and Haagan Dazs.... "Eat food." Right. He gave me a packet of Chinese tea and told me to drink some every day. He also told me about the weekly qigong classes he gives right there in his apartment. I've never been attracted to the gentle side of martial arts but I'm a big believer in acupressure and I believe that good energy flow is important. I told him I'd be there. One hour every Thursday night.

I want to thank Art, Sherry and Dr. Les at the Institute for their help so afterwards I went to my favorite place to buy leis. Chinatown. I love that our Chinatown isn't for tourists, it's the real thing. I don't get down there now as much as I did when I worked nearby and could walk there but it's the best place to buy leis.

I spent over an hour but found three that were inexpensive but awesome. The florist packed them for shipping and told me I should drive them to the airport post office to get them on their way today. The leis cost $30; shipping cost $50!

* * *

Thursday. Thanksgiving morning. It's a crisp fall day in most parts of the country and there was a dip in the weather here, too – from mid-80s to upper 70s. I love sleeping with just the screen of the sliding glass door closed so I wake up to the warm air on my skin. I love waking up with the sun shining.

I got up and went to the bathroom to pee but at the doorway my knees gave out and I dropped like a rock onto the hard tile floor. I sat there, fully conscious and alert but helpless, while my head banged and banged and banged against the door. I knew I was having a convulsion. Finally I stopped banging and eventually I was able to get up and make my shaky way to the toilet. My right knee hurt and I looked down at a quarter-size bump. My big toe ached where the toenail had bent back. Blood leaked out from under the nail. I wrapped it in a Band-Aid.

I was amazingly calm, didn't call the doctor and wouldn't have even if it hadn't been a holiday. I blame the convulsion on my low weight and maybe some kind of imbalance from my diet and I don't think a bunch of tests would have told me anything that would have made a difference. And besides, tonight I'm going up the mountain to John's for Thanksgiving dinner.

* * *

Friday. I love spending holidays and other impromptu party times with John and his friends. They're fun, a close-knit group and some of the best food and best red wine in town ends up on his table. I wouldn't want to have to drive to the top of Tantalus every day, wouldn't want to live in a big old wooden house that would take forever to clean, wouldn't want to have to take short showers and water plants with bath water, wouldn't want to have to pay the water truck to fill the holding tank when it doesn't rain enough to fill the catchment, but I love going there for parties. Especially when it's chilly and John lights a fire in the huge fireplace.

Sometimes I try to imagine what it would have been like when the Wilder family used the house for a summer retreat. The house is huge. Four bedrooms and two bathrooms (one with a huge, claw-foot tub) on the entry level, then a huge kitchen, dining room, summer room, and giant living room on the second floor. From the east side of the second floor you can look down into Manoa Valley and the University of Hawaii. Slightly right is Diamond Head Crater and just beyond that, the blue Pacific stretches for thousands of miles.

John tells guests that when the Wilder family had the house built (early 1900s), construction workers had to bring lumber, including 40-foot beams for the ceiling, up on horse-drawn wagons. I wonder what life would have been like here then. Good, I think. At least for the Wilders. I wish I were part of a simpler life. On one level I know I could be, I'd just have to let go of doing and wanting a lot of things I do and want. I need to let go of thinking I have to be so busy.

It was great to be at John's having fun even though I couldn't eat most of the food. For the first time, I didn't touch the cheese or chips and dips, didn't eat even one bite of creamy, buttery mashed potatoes. I didn't drink the luscious red wine, and I didn't eat the scrumptious desserts. I'm proud of myself.

* * *

Saturday. This afternoon I had a phone appointment for Sherry to do an intuitive reading. She told me once before that she doesn't usually do medical readings but when she does, they're always right. I punched in her number and waited for her to get centered and start talking. After a minute she said she saw a few straggler cancer cells in my right breast but she feels that I can move them on by eating a lot of green food.

I felt myself relax without realizing I'd been tense. Every time someone tells me I don't have cancer anymore (which she pretty much did) I think I believe it a little more.

She says she feels that I work too hard (true), that I spend too much time in my masculine energy trying to make things happen and that my body would like me to use my feminine energy more, look for ways to slow down, soften up, take care of myself for a change. I know this is right. I know exactly when I started to get tough – it was when I worked at the Auto Club.

I loved being a corporate writer, enjoyed being in the inner circle, enjoyed the challenge of getting so much done. But I remember going to a librarian's luncheon honoring a writer friend and feeling the gentle energy of the group; I realized at that luncheon that the make-it-happen person I'd become wasn't really who I was and that one day I'd want to gentle down, not cram so much efficiency into every minute.

I want to be mellow and have time to take care of myself instead of pushing through everything just because I can.

I remember once, after I'd worked at the Auto Club about three years, my heart started pounding – for days – and I couldn't slow it down. Finally I called one of the company's EAP counselors and he asked me what I did to take care of myself. I asked him what he meant. He asked when the last time was that I'd taken a trip by myself or bought a bottle of wine to enjoy just by myself. The idea had never occurred to me. Asked the same question today I'd have to say I still don't do much to pamper myself. And yet now I'm free all day to choose what to do. Why do I choose to work so hard?

* * *

December, 1997

Monday. I call his office every week but I still don't have an appointment with Dr. Pfeil so I dug out the phone book again. I found a doctor in Kapahulu who does chelation therapy – that's supposed to remove heavy metals from your blood, which is supposed to help circulation. I called to talk to the doctor and he's out of town but his staff invited me to stop by for a visit. The waiting room reminded me of a scene from a sci-fi film; patients sat on sheet-draped lounge chairs, reading or sleeping while an IV dripped from a bag on a pole into their arm. Nope. It doesn't feel right.

* * *

Tuesday. I went to see Dr. Kim, a doctor I found who's been trained to offer oxygen therapy treatment. His English isn't very good but it's good enough that we could work together. He said if I decide to do the oxygen therapy he'll call the doctor who trained him and ask for help calculating the dosage. On the plus side, he's an M.D. so my insurance will cover at least the office visit part. But I'm not sure. When in doubt, don't, is my motto. I told him I'd call if I decided to do it. I spent today curled up on my bed reading.

* * *

Friday. I got a letter in the mail from an elderly lady with spidery handwriting who wrote that she'd gotten my name and address from one of the women I'd talked to and she wanted to share her cancer experience with me. She encouraged me to drink Essiac tea. She had, lots of it, and 15 years later she's still well. I called to thank her for writing and we talked for a while. Mary Lou recommended the tea and I'm actually already drinking it several times a week but I don't feel like I should rely on that alone.

Yesterday a friend of another friend took me to a Japanese healing center in Aiea. Adrianne said she'd been diagnosed with breast cancer two years ago, had had a biopsy that was positive for cancer, but hadn't been willing to have a lumpectomy until she could get a change in her insurance. In the meantime, she'd been invited to the Japanese center and had recognized it was her spiritual home. She joined and began doing the energy healing for others. Two months later her insurance was arranged and she went back to her doctor for the lumpectomy but a new mammogram showed the lump was gone.

I'm attracted to the ritual, the treatment is pleasant and everyone made me feel very welcome, but I don't feel like it's right for me. Adrienne offered to work with me even if I didn't want to go back to the center but I feel I can do as much on my own with my Reiki. Which reminds me, I need to do it more.

What am I going to do for money? Someone suggested I take advantage of my insurance and see a therapist to help me with stress, to help me not be so terrified of going back to work. I feel that work leads to stress and stress leads to cancer and until I can learn how to respond differently to workplace stress, I'm not safe there.

The therapist I chose told me that if I were diagnosed with post-traumatic stress syndrome, I'd qualify for disability insurance and have six months with at least some income while I figure out what to do next. The thing is, he's a psychologist. I'll need a psychiatrist to make the diagnosis. He gave me the name of a referral and I made an appointment.

* * *

Saturday. Every once in a while I remind myself to relax and take advantage of living in Hawaii so this afternoon I went to a beach in Waimanalo where rows of pine trees grow in the sand just a few feet from the turquoise water. I love that I can park in the shade of those trees a rock's throw from the water and write or read, sheltered from the wind. I took a book on meditation and spent an hour there. Interesting. I love it, but I only spent an hour. Why am I so restless? Why do I always think I have to be doing something "productive"? And why do I think that relaxing and taking care of myself isn't?

* * *

Monday. Dr. Martin called to ask if I'd reconsidered the mastectomy. I heard her voice and the next instant my body was tight, all my muscles tensed but I told her no. She said that she'll need me to sign a statement saying I've chosen not to follow her advice. I don't know if I really have to, but I can understand her position so I said I will. I hung up the phone praying I'm doing the right thing. I hate it that any contact with allopathic doctors, even just on the phone, still scares me. How long before I'm not always perched on the edge of fear?

* * *

Wednesday. Dr. Martin's letter came today. I put it on the coffee table unopened, and tried to ignore it for a few hours. Turns out I get just as anxious about mail from allopathic doctors as I do about phone calls. Times like this I'm glad I don't drink. If I did, I'd anesthetize myself deeply.

When I finally opened the letter I skimmed the words then signed and took it out to the mailbox to be rid of it.

I've been very open minded with all the alternative cancer therapies I've looked at but nothing has felt right. I'm not going to exist on a diet of juiced carrots, I'm not going to join the Japanese group in Aiea. I'm not going to have chelation therapy and I'm not going to do the oxygen thing with Dr. Kim. Good to know. But what *am* I going to do?

I'm still reading and rereading Goldberg's book and I'm more and more interested in herbs and naturopathic remedies. Dr. Pfeil's receptionist is still trying to fit me into his busy schedule but I'm getting frustrated. When it takes so long to squeeze me in, I wonder will he have time in his busy schedule to actually come up with a protocol of care for me?

Am I trying to over-manage my life when I should be trusting the Universe? Maybe. But I have to take care of myself, I can't just wait for something to drop in my lap. I tried that years ago freelance writing. I waited for the Universe to give me direction and I think it was waiting for me to give it some. I barely earned enough to pay the mortgage and eat.

I got out the phone book and started calling other naturopaths, asking what they'd do if they had a cancer patient. Several didn't have the slightest idea but then one seemed quite intelligent and I've decided to give up on Pfeil and see this other guy, instead.

* * *

Thursday. Interesting. Not 24 hours later, Dr. Pfeil's receptionist called to say she's made a space for me tomorrow. Suddenly I have two appointments and that feels almost more stressful than not having any! Now I have to choose. I can't just chalk her phone call up to co-incidence – I don't believe in coincidences – so I tried to figure out what it all means.

Am I supposed to go to Dr. Pfeil? Did the Universe get me that appointment because he's the one I'm supposed to see? I meditated about which to choose, remember he's come highly recommended, and cancelled my appointment with the other doctor.

* * *

Friday. Nearly two months after hearing about Dr. Pfeil, I finally met him. He spent more than an hour asking questions, his pen flying over pages of paper. I'm impressed. He asked about my diet, scribbled it all down, then told me what he wants me to eat (fresh vegetables and fruits, certain fish but not bottom-feeders) and drink (purified water). He sent me downstairs to the lab for a blood test and told me to make an appointment for next week.

Money is on my mind a lot. Organic fruits and vegetables are expensive. Every month I'm spending about twice what comes in.

* * *

Saturday. Today I had a major, *major* epiphany. The instant it came I felt myself, my body and my mind, become peaceful. All the fear melted away. After three or four minutes the bliss of discovery lightened, but I don't think the imprint will ever totally go away. This whole cancer thing isn't about me living or dying, it isn't about my body at all. It's an opportunity for me to stick to what I think I should do instead of giving up, being a victim, giving in to people who tell me that only *they* have the answers. Maybe I will die, but if I follow my own guidance in this I will have accomplished one of the lessons I came to this life to learn.

This lesson has come up a lot. All my life I've had strong convictions. I've fought for them but only up to a point. Eventually, I just give up. Either "they" convince me they're right and I'm wrong, they convince me I'm being unreasonable, or I just get tired and give in.

I'd tried to get my parents to let me have a say in what happened in my life. I'd talked and argued and fought and then given up when nothing I did made a difference.

I'd gotten married and tried to be in a mutually nurturing relationship but my ex couldn't hear when I was unhappy. Eventually I gave up there, too.

I'd let myself become a workaholic at the Auto Club, letting other people convince me that's what "good" employees did. I'd stayed, even though I'd realized the high-pressure life wasn't good for me.

I'd tried to work with Gunther, I'd tried to avoid Gunther and eventually I'd given up and become a victim. I'd rationalized not leaving my job by convincing myself I was being smart to hang on till Christmas – even though some days I could barely force myself to go to the office.

But now I get it. I'll survive, or not, but that's not what this is about. What's important is my spirit lesson to follow the path *I* think I need to be on and not give in to what other people think I should do.

* * *

Monday. Today I drove over to Kailua to have lunch with Karen between her massage clients. She told me about a young client of hers, a boy, who has a tumor in his brain who visualized a wall surrounding and containing it. Several months later his doctor said an X-ray showed a wall around the cancer...! I promise, I'll do more visualization.

I remember what cancer cells look like from a lecture at the Institute so when I got home from Karen's I turned off the phone, sat in my rocker and visualized any that might still be there wafting away in a cloud of something purple. Boring. I visualized them getting gobbled by Pac-Man. For about a minute. Somehow that didn't appeal to me, either. I've read that some people create soldiers who battle the cancer cells but I don't like violence so I don't want to do that. I was mulling what else I could do when I heard the words, again: *It's time to go.*

Then it hit me that the words don't have to be about *me* going, I can make them be about it being time for the *cancer cells* to go! Sometimes when I come up with just the right idea I can imagine my wiser self smiling excitedly and saying, "Yeah, that's it!" And that's what my wiser self did. I knew, I could feel, this was the perfect way to visualize any remnant cancer cells going – calmly but firmly. *Thank you for the gifts you've brought, now it's time to go.*

* * *

Tuesday. This morning I pushed past my urge to do something productive, packed a book on meditations and a cooler of healthy food and drove to Kapolei to relax. The highway leeward curves through small communities and ends at the west end of the island in Waianae. The beaches are beautiful, but it's not smart to park where you can't watch your car – the crime rate is high out there so I rarely go. But Kapolei is a spiffy new community 20 minutes east with a luxury hotel and man-made lagoons to swim in.

The lagoon by the hotel is my favorite and I dragged a lawn chair under a coconut tree. I watched kids splashing in the shallow water for awhile then tried to meditate. Why is it so hard for me to just sit? Why do I always have to be doing something productive?

When I got home the phone message light was blinking. The owner had left another message asking when I'm coming back to work. I called back and left a message on her machine saying I just don't know. I just don't know. It's been almost two months and I still feel very fragile, emotionally. I know I'm not strong enough to handle the stress and I still don't know how I can do that job without stress.

* * *

Wednesday. The more I read, the more convinced I am that there's a conspiracy by the drug companies to keep the public from knowing that not everyone with cancer needs their expensive drugs. It makes me furious but anger isn't good for me and as one of my friends reminded me, it isn't my job to fight the drug companies, it's my job to get well.

Mary Lou told me about a chiropractor who does energy work and since my insurance covers some chiropractic, I made an appointment. We'll see.

Larry has called nearly every day since I got back from California. We've driven to the Windward side to window shop at Windward Mall; we've watched fireworks at the Hilton then gone to Coconut Willy's to dance. We've driven around the island like tourists, I showed him a nature preserve on the beach by Aina Haina he'd never seen, we stood on the bluff looking down at Hanauma Bay and pigged out on shrimp scampi at the Shrimp Truck.

It would be so wonderful to have a nice man in my life permanently. I've gotten just about everything I've ever wanted except a man who I want to love who will love me back. Larry says he does, but he's also decided to go to the mainland for Christmas to visit the woman he's not sure he's over. He tells me that he loves me but she's safe. After so many years he knows her inside and out and how much does he know about me, really?

My whole life right now is about being brave, risking in order to have what I want, so I don't admire him for talking about making a decision because it might be safe. Enough! It's important right now that I eliminate as much stress as I can so I have to forget about him. I told myself at the beginning that it wouldn't be healthy for me to get too attached to him. Sometimes I'm too optimistic. But it's still possible that he might choose me....

* * *

Thursday. I hate doing breast exams, am afraid of them, actually. I don't exactly think I'll find a lump but I'm afraid I might. Or I'm afraid I might find something that feels like a lump that isn't and it'll scare me to death anyway. And today I felt something that caused that cave-in feeling in my stomach. I don't remember a lump there before. I want to think it's nothing. I actually *do* think it's nothing but what if.... I hate feeling so afraid. I hate carrying so much dread. It would be so easy to just give in and tell Dr. Martin to do what she wants to do but I'm not going to. I remind myself the lesson is for me not to give in but I did make an appointment for her to check the lump.

I went to Pecos River Café tonight. Sometimes I long for the old days, dancing in California where there were hundreds of good dancers, where the bands were great and they played music that was perfect to dance to and not so loud that you couldn't hold a three-word conversation. Honolulu bands seem determined to make us all deaf.

Larry wasn't there. We went for a long walk this afternoon and he's on a plane to the mainland to see if he's still in love. I hope he isn't but I think he will be. She's safe. I will not think about him for the next month and when he comes back, we'll see.

* * *

Friday. Dr. Martin had an I-hope-you-realize-you're-making-a-big-mistake look on her face but she examined me carefully and didn't seem worried. She did schedule me for a mammogram, though. I'm relieved she wasn't concerned, but am wondering why she ordered an X-ray then. I went downstairs to X-ray and then sat on a bench in the sun for a few minutes to let some of the anxiety go.

Later I went back to Dr. P to hear the results of my blood test and to have a test that will guide him in my therapy.

He took me into a room, sat me in a comfortable recliner chair and put small sensors, like EKG disks, in various places on my body. He pushed a few buttons and we watched the monitor as this specially designed software scanned my body for vibrations. Once he knows what's there that shouldn't be there, he'll know what to prescribe to flush it out.

In the biography I wrote about Einstein I talked about his discovery that colors vibrate at different frequencies. It makes sense to me that if colors vibrate differently, so do things in our cells. Anyway, the test showed there are insecticides (probably from my early days in Hawaii when I used to chase cockroaches with a steady stream of Raid till they dropped) and pesticides (how many bushels of fruits and veggies have I eaten without washing?) still in my body. There are industrial pollutants and cosmetic pollutants stored in my cells. I showed gluten reactions, allergies to dust and grass and cashews. Good to know.

I told him about my latest mammogram and he wants me to go see a doctor friend of his. He said it might be good to talk to an M.D. who's open to patients working with a naturopath, just to get his input.

I came home with a paper bag full of pills; anti-inflammatories and immune supporters, pills to eliminate unneeded estrogens and some pills to support digestion.

I feel like this is the right thing to be doing. Doesn't it make more sense to flush toxins and boost my immune system than to have more surgery and subject myself to something that can and probably would burn the wrong thing and drugs that will poison everything?

I feel so powerful when I'm working at getting well naturally, but it can all take a dive in an instant. This afternoon Dr. Martin's receptionist called to say the mammogram looked okay, but the radiologist wants to do a magnification X-ray, maybe ultra sound, maybe biopsy, just to be sure. I took myself out for a brisk walk to de-stress. It's hard to believe that he isn't asking for more information for a reason.

* * *

Monday. I went to the chiropractor, Dr. Andy. He's a local Japanese man who closes his eyes while he reads my energy. He waves his arms over various parts of my body and when he pokes me he always finds a spot that hurts but I do feel more balanced afterwards.

Andy told me about a group that does an energy exercise form called Kalimasada that meets in a park on King Street every Tuesday evening. I'm willing to look at anything so I agreed to go and see what it's all about.

* * *

Tuesday. I had the second mammogram and the ultrasound test and the technician casually said, "I think what you're feeling are the clips." Clips? What clips? Dr. Martin didn't tell me she used metal clips as sutures. I thanked the technician profusely and floated out of the office.

It's hard to feel Christmassy when it's 85 degrees every day and I can't even eat Christmas cookies. I treated myself to my monthly Butterfinger, though. Woo woo.

* * *

Wednesday. Didn't think doctors worked on Christmas Eve but it seems they do. I went to see Dr. Martin to hear what she thinks about the latest mammogram.

She said, "The scar tissue looks fine but you still need more treatment. These lumps don't feel suspicious but remember, the other lumps didn't all feel suspicious, either." I tried to close my ears without using my fingers. *Tell me, Karin Ireland, did you always know....* She might have noticed me trying to ignore her because she suddenly changed gears and told me about a trial procedure being evaluated on Oahu – there's only one doc doing it but he's right across the hall.

The idea is that they inject dye at the site of the former tumor and then after some time they take an X-ray to see which lymph node the dye drained to. Next, they surgically remove that lymph node and see if there's cancer. If the cancer moved, it would move to the same node the dye did so if the pathology report comes back negative for cancer, it indicates that the cancer probably didn't spread. If the lymph node shows cancer…well… that wouldn't be good.

I agreed to consider it. I feel my body saying, no, though. Why? Because I trust that I'm okay, am going to be okay? Because I'm afraid that it would show that I'm not?

I went shopping and tried on a few new tops. I looked in the mirror and asked myself, am I so vain that I'm willing to die just to look good? What if it were my ovaries…something that wouldn't show? Wouldn't it still depend on how likely the chances are that there's still cancer there? There's just no way to know anything for sure and since I can't, I'm recommitting to honoring my feelings and trusting that my body is giving me the right signals.

When I got home there was a letter from a friend, a breast cancer survivor, who warned me that I'm taking a big risk if I don't do the traditional care. Not what I needed.

I puttered around feeling lonely. Tricia called and told me how much she supports the way I'm getting rid of my cancer and that means a lot to me. She said I am an inspiration. I basked in her approval and wished we didn't live so far apart.

I hadn't planned to go up to John's for Christmas dinner because I'm feeling depressed, but around 3 o'clock he called.

"You have to come," he said. "I'm cooking fish, and it won't be the same here without you." It was sweet, and I really *wanted* to go so I did.

Koz, one of John's friends, is Japanese. She does a daily radio broadcast to Japan via phone from Honolulu and tonight she did her program from our dinner table and passed the mike around.

"Merry Christmas."

"Happy New Year."

"Mele Kalikimaka."

I'm not sure how many listeners understood us but we had fun. After dinner we opened gifts, sang some songs and it was cold enough (okay, cool enough) to have a fire. I'm glad I went.

* * *

Friday. Today I had an appointment with the psychiatrist to see if he'll support my request for disability insurance. I prayed he would. Even though I think I'm doing pretty well, I still equate cancer with stress and stress with work.

"I know the emotional turmoil you're going through," he said, "because my wife had breast cancer a few years ago. I convinced her to have a double mastectomy so she wouldn't have to go through it again."

I forced myself to keep my face blank but at that moment I felt sorrier for her than for myself. Though I miss the support of a husband or steady boyfriend, I'm glad I'm alone so I can make my own decisions. I think about Kathy, and know that having a mastectomy doesn't mean you definitely won't get the cancer back. I didn't say anything, though, and he approved me for disability. Yippee! There'll be money for food and rent for a while.

He's given me the names of a gaggle of other doctors who he thinks might be able to help me get some perspective on my overwork/perfectionist issues so I can find a job I'm better suited to and so I can know when to quit if it's not working for me. Another project. Who should I choose?

* * *

Monday. Dr. P had me do a gallbladder flush and it was terrible! I had to drink stuff that made me feel like I was poisoning myself. I hope his tests show it worked because I never want to do it again! I'm going to Dr. Andy every week for energy balancing. I'm going to Master Wong's qigong classes, too. My big toenail fell off and underneath there's a layer of tough skin. It looks weird so I painted it red to match the others.

* * *

Tuesday. He's just like all the others, this doctor friend of Dr. P's. "I don't feel anything, but your surgeon didn't get clean margins...you should have the mastectomy."

Ugh. I'm depressed. But, really, *what's different?* I know that Dr. Martin didn't get clean margins and she'd recommended a mastectomy and I said no. Why do I let it upset me to hear it again?

I finally went to the Kalimasada class Andy told me about. It seems a lot like Tai Chi while holding your breath for longer than I can. I don't like it, but will give it a few more sessions before I drop out.

Tonight I was channel surfing and I found a special on Caroline Myss. She talked about not letting your power escape and it reminded me, *again,* to call on the cameraman more often. *Tell me, Karin Ireland, did you always know you'd be rich and famous?*

As good as I get controlling where my mind and energy goes, fear still manages to stab me at odd moments. Am I going to survive this cancer or am I going "home?" I just don't know. But I did tell God, if it's home, I insist on seeing Tricia first. We talk on the phone at least once a week and she's a wonderful support. She sends me little gifts, cute cards, I just wish it wasn't so expensive to visit each other in person.

* * *

Wednesday. New Year's Eve. I had an appointment with Dr. P. I finished the contents of the small vials he gave me to flush out toxins and he gave me the second batch. More small vials, liquid to drop under my tongue every morning. I got refills of the supplements I'm running out of and am thankful my dad is paying for them.

This afternoon I went to a party on the North Shore. I'm amazed how much money people are willing to spend on fireworks. When I got there the neighborhood was already gray with smoke. The host said his neighbors had been shooting fireworks since morning. Where do they get the money for it?

I'm glad I made the effort to come, but sometimes being in a crowd, I feel more lonely. One guy did talk to me most of the time and he was nice, but when he asked if I got out this way much in a hint-hint kind of way I said no. I don't want to fall for someone who lives on the North Shore. I really think that if Mr. Perfect showed up on my doorstep tomorrow the smartest thing I could do would be to say come back, try again in six months.

At midnight my hosts launched some rockets and handed us all sparklers and half an hour later, I left. Didn't want to be driving on that dark, lonely country road when all the drunks were ready to go home. As Waialua faded in my rear-view mirror I pulled over along the dark highway and looked back. The whole sky was bright with sparkling multi-colored lights.

* * *

January, 1998

Thursday. New Year's Day. It's been two-and-a-half months and I'm still okay. I feel good, optimistic, and I plan to wrap up all my projects in a day or so and then spend more time being and far less doing. Interesting that I've been a workaholic for at least a dozen years and now that I don't actually have a job, I'm overworked with projects I don't actually *have* to do!

I didn't have the energy to send out Christmas cards, but I'm feeling stronger now and I want to say thanks to everyone who's been so great, so today I spent about four hours writing a letter with details of my progress. I made a pot of soup. I went through closets for things to take to Goodwill and I cleaned house. Oops, projects?

I can never be completely project free, I think not having anything to do would make me feel restless. I need money, though, so I've decided to focus on writing.

I wrote a query for an article about my experience with cancer and sent it to several women's magazines. I've always thought I might like to write a novel; wonder what it would be about?

* * *

Saturday. Today I went to a children's book writing conference and got re-inspired. When I first started writing I longed to write charming pictures books but they're not easy. About 10 years later I wrote one that sold, *Wonderful Nature, Wonderful You,* then went back to writing self-help books. I can still remember the calm feeling I had at the librarian's luncheon *years* ago; maybe if I spend my time writing children's books I'll slow down and become less driven.

Most of the time I'm feeling pretty comfortable choosing alternative medicine, but then this afternoon a friend of dance-buddy Art's returned my phone call from about a month ago. Wish she hadn't. She told me she'd had breast cancer and she went with the full allopathic treatment – mastectomy, radiation, chemo, the works. She warned me that lobular cancer is the most dangerous kind because it pops up at random places later and she thinks it's dangerous not to follow the M.D.'s advice.

I didn't feel like I could say *please don't tell me those things, I called you ages ago,* so I let her go on and on while mentally interjecting *but not me* into her warnings. I hung up and worried again about whether I'm making the right decision. What if I'm wrong about the choice being part of my spiritual path? I don't think I am, though, and I'm committed to following my feelings. I only worried for a couple of hours. Maybe I'm getting better at this?

* * *

Monday. I feel like I'm in good hands with Dr. Pfeil and I've pretty much exhausted the cancer cure bookshelf at every bookstore in town but bookstores feel like a cozy haven to me so I spend a lot of time at one or the other of them. Today I found myself drawn to *Practical Intuition* by Laura Day. Intuition is something I've always been interested in and I know it works for me, but so far it always just comes to me unexpectedly. What I want to know is how I can hold a question and summon an answer. It looks like the book can teach me to do that so I bought it.

* * *

Wednesday. This afternoon I went for a walk along the beach with Alexis, who had been diagnosed with breast cancer and had had a lumpectomy. Her doctors told her they hadn't gotten clean margins and recommended a mastectomy and chemotherapy and she'd said okay. She had the mastectomy and the pathology report showed there hadn't been any cancer left. Alexis says she read in Susan Love's breast book that that happens. Even after that, her doctor *still* recommended chemotherapy and she had a few sessions. She was nauseous after each treatment and started finding clumps of hair on her shower floor. After the third treatment she told her oncologist she wanted to stop and said he seemed relieved. Did he know he was poisoning her for no good reason except to do what everybody else did?

That could have been me!

I asked if she was angry at losing her breast for no reason and she said no, that she believed she was here this lifetime to experience everything and that was just one of the things for her to experience. That's a wonderful attitude but I know I would have been homicidal if that had happened to me. I would have never forgiven the doctors or myself. Every time I looked at or even thought about my body I would have felt like such a victim.

I went to my qigong class with Master Wong tonight and I've pretty much gotten the basics. The trouble is that when I relax and do the moves with my eyes closed, focusing on the energy, I can feel it flow but I can't remember all the moves in exactly the right order. I open my eyes to peek and I'm not where everybody else is. When I keep my eyes open and my brain engaged I can follow him, but then I don't feel the energy. I think he changes the moves slightly every couple of times and that doesn't help.

* * *

Monday. Tricia will be here in two days so I dedicated the afternoon to cleaning house. An hour later my tiny apartment was spotless. I vow to have a second bedroom for her to sleep in the next time she comes and I also vow to be brave enough to tell my neighbors to be quiet the next time they keep me awake until 3 a.m.

* * *

Wednesday. Tricia's here! The day was perfect. The 80-degree shorts-and-T-top weather was 40 degrees warmer than the jeans-and-jacket weather she left in Chico. I gave myself an extra half hour going to the airport so I could stop in Chinatown to enjoy my lei ritual: Go Beretania to Maunakea and turn left. Park illegally just around the corner, turn flashers on. Start at the shop on the corner and if I don't find the perfect lei, zig-zag on foot across the street, in and out of shops along Maunakea. Turn left at Hotel Street, left at Smith Street, left back onto Beretania. About 15 shops in all. At the 8th shop I found a beautiful lei of fluffy white dendrobiums and baby pink rosebuds for $7.

I love the airport signs that read "Departures, Arrivals," and "Lei Stands." I love everything about Hawaii that makes it different, special.

It only took me two times around the airport to find the right parking area. Ta da! In the airport they play Hawaiian music, which I think is really smart. I am so glad I get to live here, so glad that when I travel I always get to come back.

Inside the arrival area I slipped the damp lei from the plastic bag and let it dangle from my arm to dry some. I moved as close as I could to the gate without blocking the flow of people coming off the plane. I'm always anxious for the first glimpse of Tricia and finally, there she was. She spotted me and smiled a big smile. I love her so much.

"Aloha," I said, slipping the lei over her head. We hugged a long time, neither really wanting to let go.

We took the freeway home to drop off her luggage then we headed for the beach. Up over the Pali and through Kailua town to Lanakai. We sat by the water and caught up on news until we got hungry and left to search for food.

It is so good to be with her. I didn't know when she went away to school that she'd like it and decide to stay.

After we got home we opened our Christmas presents. She gave me a gorgeous blanket, fuzzy, forest green, the kind I have often drooled over but never bought. Perfect for winter nights that drop to the mid-sixties. She also gave me a pretty glass angel to hang on my window, an angel to keep me safe. I hope....

"You've lost a lot of weight," she said after hugging me Merry Christmas.

I asked her if I look too thin. I'm gaining it back slowly but I kind of like my sleek hips.

"No, but your back is all bones."

Tonight we walked in Waikiki. Up Kalakaua from the zoo past the police station, then past exclusive shops that boast trendy designer clothes and shoes and bags, the most expensive cameras, luggage and jewelry. For the less affluent, there are stores that sell cosmetics, T-shirts and magnets. Japanese restaurants tempt Japanese tourists, McDonald's comforts unimaginative mainlanders, and two Haagen Dazs ice cream shops draw everyone in at least once. This could be Anyplace, USA.

But turn left at Seaside, walk down the access walk beside the Outrigger Hotel and the beach sand is still warm, the ocean laps gently against the shore, Hawaiian music drifts from the ocean-front hotels and lights curve gently along the shore all the way to a dark bulk that is Diamond Head. This could only be Waikiki.

* * *

Wednesday. It's always hard to see Tricia go but I'm thankful we had this week together. If she lived here maybe I'd play more. Okay, I promise, PROMISE I'll take more time to play by myself, slow down, recreate my life on a gentler level. Why is this so hard for me to do?

* * *

Thursday. I vowed to get back at writing first thing after Tricia left but this morning I felt really tired so I stayed in bed till noon. I still try to act like I've always acted, which is tireless, but I just don't have as much energy as I used to. And that's okay.

* * *

Friday. I think it's interesting that I've promised myself to eat better (starting tomorrow or next week) for most of my life and never actually been able to do it. I could go into a store holding the thought, *I will not have anything to snack on* and within minutes I'd forget all the reasons or rationalize them away and I'd end up at the check-out counter with two empty Butterfinger wrappers or two cookie or donut papers or the wrapping from a Twinkie three-pack, in my hand, hating myself for my lack of willpower, *again!*

Yet the *instant* I learned I had cancer I went cold turkey off everything. What does that tell you? And I'm still doing good – still on my vegan, no wheat/caffeine/sugar diet.

Unfortunately, I'm not doing well in the exercise department. I want to do qigong more but I keep putting it off. I want to meditate but it's easier to sit at my computer and write. Writing nurtures my workaholic self. But I've started a picture book I think could be fun:

> *If you take your pig out shopping,*
> *Don't take him to the mall.*
> *He'll play in the dirt in the planter outside*
> *And you won't get to shop at all.*
>
> *Don't take your elephant down to the beach,*
> *No matter how much he begs.*
> *After hours of rubbing on bottles of lotion,*
> *You'll barely have covered his legs.*

* * *

Saturday. I take the pills Pfeil prescribes faithfully. Every 12 days I get out a small muffin tin and count out pills to take with breakfast, pills to take between breakfast and lunch, pills to take with lunch, between lunch and dinner, with dinner and before bed. I scoop each pile into a baggie and mark it with black ink.

My friend Karen consciously blesses her food before she eats it; Tricia blesses the pills she takes. I think I could do that – would it make them more effective? But I forget. Can anyone really do everything, *everything*, that might help them be healthier? To work so hard at being healthy seems to put so much focus on the opposite alternative, being *un*healthy. I could be doing Reiki, too. But I tell myself there's room to just trust, too, trust that what I'm led to do is what I need to do.

* * *

Thursday. Today I went for a walk down Kalakaua to watch the tourists in Waikiki and, ta da, get my monthly candy bar. Why is it that Butterfinger bars are always broken? No matter, it doesn't change how the chocolate melts on my tongue, how the sugary center crunches deliciously between my back teeth and then slowly slides down my throat. It was wonderful. I parked by the zoo and walked all the way to the Hilton Hotel. Walking is the one exercise I seem willing to do.

Tonight I had the strongest urge to go to a bookstore so I went. I looked at two more books on intuition and ended up buying them both plus a magazine called *Intuition*. I'm fascinated with the subject and I wish I were one of those people who had impressively psychic experiences.

An ad at the back of the magazine caught my eye and I kept turning back to it.

"Get a college degree in Intuition. Bachelor, Master's, Ph.D." Greenwich University is on the Big Island, I could take classes in their distance learning program and wouldn't actually have to go there, and, and this is the big attraction, the Master's Degree in Intuition includes seminars with Caroline Myss!

The snag is that it's expensive and I'm not working. Would it be worth the serious dent it would make in my savings account? I ask myself, money not an object, what would I do with my life? Would I learn to be impressively intuitive and somehow turn it into a job? I just don't know.

I try to meditate and let my intuition give me the answer.

* * *

Friday. The picture book is progressing. Where do these rhymes come from? Not from me, I'm pretty sure. It's like I just put my attention in a certain "space" and they pop into my head.

> *If you walk in the park at night before dinner,*
> *Think twice before bringing your 'gator.*
> *A lady once took hers out for a walk,*
> *And her 'gator got hungry and ate her!*

Ideas for self-help books pop into my head all the time but all my queries are answered by editors who say "it isn't quite right for our list." Then I go to the bookstore and see books that are similar but not nearly as good. So frustrating. But I keep trying and today I sent Julie a query with another five ideas.

Larry is back and was at Rumours but he didn't call during the week so I guess I know what he decided. It's over and I am *definitely* not going to think about him any more.

* * *

Saturday. Today, as part of my "Remember you live Hawaii" (sic) program, I called the concierge at the Turtle Bay Hilton in the country for a weather check.

"It look good. Little clouds, mostly sun. C'mon over."

I filled a bag with carrots, apples, almonds and bottled water. No more stopping at Starbucks for a traveler cup and a muffin.

I love the windward coast, the side of the island that is still rural. Except for the hotel, it's mostly just houses and empty space after you leave Kaneohe until Haleiwa.

I passed the Shrimp Truck without stopping. I
didn't stop for a soda. I munched on carrots, instead. Yum.
Not fair that some people can eat whatever they want, do
whatever they want and never have a problem.

Sometimes I wonder how the Turtle Bay Hilton
survives. It's never crowded – it's too far from most of
the things tourists come to Hawaii to do but I guess it
does have a good golf course. I found a lawn chair on the
bluff past the bar and dragged it under a palm tree and
watched the surfers catching long rides on the small three-
to four-foot waves.

When I got bored, I went to the other side of the
hotel and sat on the bay side. I watched the waves roll
in and out and tried to use them to meditate. I watched
couples and families and wished I had someone to share
Hawaii with.

* * *

February, 1998

Friday. February has started off well. I'm still
comfortable with Dr. Pfeil, still resigned to choosing
almonds over candy, herb tea over coffee, salted bell peppers over potato chips or Fritos, real food over frozen stuff
loaded with sugar, fat or salt. To be honest, salmon tastes
good, trout pan fried in olive oil is delicious, bell peppers,
chilled yams, and carrots are fine to munch on. I'm even
starting to like soy yogurt and organic popcorn popped
in olive oil.

This morning I got to stay in bed late without feeling guilty. I had a new test scheduled at Dr. P's for 10:30
where he would record the heat of my body in its natural
state and then again after it had been cooled. He told me

not to do anything that could affect my body temperature – no shower, no hot or cold foods, no tight-fitting clothes, no elastic waistbands, no bra.

I perched in the waiting room on the edge of a chair so I wouldn't create any hot spots on my back. When it was my turn, the first part was to stand nude in a treatment room while Dr. P moved a wand over my body, noting my internal heat pattern as he moved it up and down my arms, legs and torso. I was very uncomfortable standing there without any clothes on. I know he's a doctor but I still felt very uncomfortable. Part two was for me to stand in the room with the thermostat turned down 15 degrees. I couldn't sit, couldn't lean against anything. After 20 minutes, Dr. P came back and moved the wand over my body again to see if any new densities (hot spots, which could indicate tumors) showed up. Thank goodness, none did.

* * *

Saturday. I'm spending hours reading my intuition books. I love the *Intuition* magazine and keep going back to the ad for the degree in intuition. Part of me is wary, but Caroline Myss is involved and I admire her a lot so I think it has to be legitimate.

I'm beginning to feel learning intuition is part of my spiritual path but I can't quite see how. I looked through the local metaphysical paper and psychics are a dime a dozen. If I take the course, how will I be different from them?

I ordered half a dozen back issues of *Intuition* and am impressed with the articles about business people, politicians, actors, directors and musicians who admit to using intuition to make important decisions. I wonder if that's what I should do – be an intuitive who helps business leaders use their intuition to make good business decisions about things like personnel, programs and products. I might like doing that....

* * *

Sunday. Even though I'm not working, I'm still *working*. I'm *always* busy. Why is that? I'm GOING TO STOP! This morning I decided to spend a whole day at the beach just sitting and thinking about my future. I even left my book in the car. It was nice for a while, then a challenge to just sit and not be doing something. I didn't have any epiphanies but I lasted a couple of hours.

* * *

Monday. This morning I decided to go to Sea Life Park. I've always wanted to, I've asked people to go with me and we never get around to it so I decided to just go by myself. I smuggled in my own lunch and was mighty glad I did. What a rip-off the food stand is. Everything costs a fortune!

The Hawaii park isn't anything like Sea World in California, but it's fun in a small-time way. Divers feed fish in the 300,000-gallon aquarium, powerful, graceful bottle-nose dolphins race and leap on cue. I got to be part of the show with sea lions!

"Who wants to come down here and say hi to this fella?" I shot my hand up.

"Come on down here," the announcer pointed at me. "Ever been kissed by a sea lion? Well, just put your head right here and don't move."

The trainer waved his hand and a cold, wet nose touched my cheek, a camera flashed and the crowd roared. Okay, they didn't roar, there weren't enough people to roar but they did clap politely. For the sea lion, I know. But it was fun.

* * *

Tuesday. This morning Dr. P gave me a bunch of

shots in my gums – they're supposed to eliminate any residual infections from previous cavities. The University of California at Irvine is doing a study to see if maitake mushrooms help eliminate cancer tumors and Dr. P tried to get me into the study but it's closed. Boo. I had my monthly blood tests to see how my NK cells are doing.

* * *

Thursday. Sid and I went to Chinatown to celebrate Chinese New Year's. I fed three dragons dollar bills so I'll have lots of good luck this year. I love the constant tata-tata-tata-tata from firecrackers. I've never been much of a firecracker fan but they just seem to belong here. People buy them in the 1,000-piece rolls and hang them over a tree branch, light the end and run. When dozens of people do that it's *really* loud! And smoky! The air turns a hazy gray-blue. Streetlights glow an eerie shade of green and orange and red. I love it. Another one of those things that makes Hawaii special.

* * *

Saturday. This afternoon Sid and I met on the beach at Magic Island for our annual Valentine's Day/Me-Moving-To-Hawaii-Anniversary sunset celebration. Three years ago at about sunset time I was climbing off the plane and ready to start a new adventure. Sid and I never seem to be in relationships on any Hallmark occasions (or any other occasions, come to think of it), so we celebrate together. After the sunset we went to Auntie Pasta's for dinner.

* * *

Sunday. I was reading on the grass at Kaimana Beach this morning when an odd man came up to me asking for sun lotion. I held out the bottle to pour some in his hand but he moved away and motioned that he wanted me to rub some on his back. Ick! No way!

He was one of the crazy people who live on the Waikiki beaches who should be safely cared for in a locked facility except that there aren't enough to hold everybody who should be there. He kept pantomiming that he wanted me to rub the lotion on him, telling me I was beautiful and trying to touch my arm or leg.

I told him he needed to go away, I told him firmly, several times but he ignored me. Finally he left, shouting obscenities over his shoulder at me. He walked on down the beach and I went back to reading. Then he came back and pretended to ignore me but sat a few feet away. I wasn't really ready to leave but I have no idea what else to do – I didn't feel comfortable sitting there right by him. Shouldn't I be able to summon up enough authority in my voice for people to know when I mean business?

* * *

Tuesday. This afternoon I saw Dr. Martin for a routine checkup. She palpated my breasts and agreed that the fibrocystic tissue is less than it was before but when I told her it was because Dr. P gave me something to flush it and I'd eliminated caffeine she looked at me like, *yeah, right*. But she's losing her power to scare me. And I'd gone prepared. I left a book in the car and afterward went to sit on the tranquil porch of the Moana Surfrider.

The Surfrider gift shop has post cards that show how the hotel looked when it was built more than a hundred years ago. It's still got a definite plantation elegance – a graceful white wooden building, long sheltered porch, a banyan tree in the beach-front patio where, they say, Robert Louis Stevenson wrote poetry.

I found a wicker chair on the porch and made myself really *look* at the endless ocean sparkling through the branches of the huge banyan tree, sea green up close and dark blue farther out. I made myself take the time to notice the way the air felt on my skin, to notice the smell of lunches being served across the patio. I wonder what it would be like to have a slow lifestyle? I wonder if people like Shakti Gawain are as tranquil as their books make them seem. And how about Deepak Chopra? Was he angry when the limo driver forgot to pick him up at the airport for his book signing? Do they spend hours meditating? Do they work on their books in leisurely three-hour blocks and then stop to sit and do nothing?

I spent the rest of the day at home burning incense and reading my new favorite book, *Conversations With God*. I bought the workbook, too, and one assignment asked me to list all the people and things that no longer served me in my life that I'm willing to let go of. I made a really long list, and can see how each thing contributes, in some way, to my stress.

I think I'm a mess of conflicts. A part of me believes I have to work 24/7 if I'm going to succeed as a writer, that the more time I spend writing the more I increase my likelihood of success. But I also believe that I shouldn't have to struggle to succeed and, indeed, that struggling is unhealthy. I believe that I'm a spiritual person and should be able to just let the drama and craziness of Gunther and the job flow off my back but I can't and I stayed because I thought there was something there I needed to learn but I didn't know what it was. I know I need to exercise but I never do. Ay yai yai.

* * *

Thursday. This afternoon I went back for my second session with Dr. Silke. She's the therapist who's going to try to help me figure out why I'm a workaholic. Actually not figure out why, I know why. I need the applause, I need the attention. I need to be able to convince myself that I'm a hard worker, a valuable person, more dedicated than anyone else. I'm still trying to disprove my childhood labels of lazy, and ungrateful.

The rational part of me knows that that was then and this is now. Now I can do half the work I actually do and still get plenty of applause. I'm friendly and fun so I get my share of attention. I'm kind, loving, loyal and a lot of other good things. I don't need to convince other people I'm valuable, I think I need to convince myself and I need to convince myself I'm valuable because of who I *am* not because of what I do.

What I need Silke to help me figure out is how to let go and not *be* a workaholic. I know it's unhealthy and unnecessary to push myself the way I do. I feel overwhelmed because I still have too many projects pulling at my attention. In self-defense, I have to say that if I sold everything I wrote or if I had a day job I loved where I was paid big bucks then maybe I'd have enough money coming in that I wouldn't feel I have to keep scrambling to make some. Or maybe if I honored myself I wouldn't be drawn to jobs that took so much out of me. Maybe I'd be calm and peaceful and fewer ideas would come but they'd be better. All I know is, I'm too busy.

On my to-do list:

Reiki – I found a really detailed book that includes (against traditional rules) all the symbols I'm supposed to hold in my mind when I'm practicing. I should memorize them.

Qigong – I'm still going to Master Wong's classes once a week and I bought a qigong book that I plan to use to practice with at home.

Intuition – I've got three books I'm reading plus I'm trying to decide if I'm supposed to sign up and get my degree in intuition.

Acupressure – I've had a book on acupressure for nearly 20 years and have use it with great success for other things – I keep meaning to look through it and see how it can help me now.

Taxes – I have to organize all my receipts and make an appointment to get them done.

Reflexology – I found a book in my bookcase that I've had for years and have wanted to explore it.

Inner child work – I believe that most of my stress comes from the ways I'm still responding to battles I had as a child (e.g. my relationship with Gunther was really about my relationship with my dad; my need to be a workaholic is about being called lazy and doing poorly in school. Now I'm demonstrating how hard a worker, how responsible I am).

Tapping – Dr. Silke showed me a method of tapping on various parts of my face and left hand while saying an affirmation to detach from old messages and fears and it works. I practice it several times a day.

Conversations With God – the book and the work-book – I love *Book One*, bought the workbook and have gotten stuck at about page 20.

Caroline Myss – I got through one of her books and want to go back and reread the parts I marked.

My own book about breast cancer – I want to write something to let other women know that alternatives are available.

Find a new job – I still dread the idea of going back to the old one.

Well, good grief! No wonder I feel like I'm not getting things done. There are 12 projects that require huge chunks of time to do well and that doesn't even include the project of shopping for healthy food and fixing it.

Oh, and meditate…so 13 things. Even if I stay busy every waking moment (which I feel like I am actually doing) there isn't time to do even half of the projects I want to do the way I want to do them. And then there are the messages I keep telling myself – that I don't need to be doing something *all the time*!

I rewrote the list and tried to prioritize:

Reiki – I'll put the book away. I made a very basic cheat sheet and posted it in the kitchen. I don't plan to use Reiki on other people and I've been taught, and believe, that the intent is more important than knowing all the symbols perfectly so I'll just relax and use what I know.

Qigong – I'll go to class and practice what I can remember and save the book for later.

Intuition – I'll put off considering school until a) I'm sure my interest is solid and b) I can comfortably afford it. In the meantime, I'll keep reading and practice when I remember.

Acupressure – stress collects in my back. I'll make notes to remember the pressure points I need and put the book away.

Taxes – a priority. Saturday I'll take my receipts and a notebook to the beach, sit in my car and get it all organized.

Reflexology – I'll forget the formal learning for now. I'll just massage my hands and feet when I think about it.

Inner child – this is important. At the most basic level, I've read that whenever I have a negative emotion I can ask my inner child what she needs and give her reassurance if I can. I don't need to buy and read another book to do that.

Silke's tapping – this is important; I need to remember to do it.

Conversations With God – I'll put away the workbook. I'll read *Book Two* as a pastime but it won't be a priority. *Book One* will be easy to refer to since I've highlighted everything that has meaning to me.

Caroline Myss – I'll put the book away and just listen to tapes when I'm in my car.

My own book about breast cancer – I'll put writing it aside, but keep writing in my journal.

Find a new job – I can put this off till the end of the month.

Meditate – I want to do that regularly.

That still seems like a lot but at least not as much as before. And I'm actually putting the books away out of sight so they don't stare accusingly.

*   *   *

Friday. This morning Dr. P's office called and gave me a serious scare. "Your latest blood work shows your natural killer cells are at 29. Last time they were 40."

My stomach did a flip flop and I did an instant replay of the last few weeks to figure out why.

"It says...uh...oh, sorry. This isn't yours. Okay, yours are fine." AAAARRRRRGGGGG!

Later I went for a walk with a buddy from Rumours and he said something interesting.

"Six years ago I had $60,000, now I have $250,000. My investments are doing well."

I'm happy for him but I can't help nagging at myself about how casually I've handled money in my life. I always keep putting off investing and accumulating money. During the time my ex and I were married we talked about replacing our ridiculously low mortgage for a higher one and using the cash to invest in other property but we never did. That little house we bought for $23,000 is probably worth over $300,000 now. If we had refinanced and bought a house or two for investment we'd have a lot of money today.

When I was first divorced, I earned what seemed like a lot of money working as a corporate writer and the house payments were tiny. But instead of investing, I spent the money on clothes, home decorations, week-long vacations at Club Meds. I grew up listening to my parents save to enjoy retirement but when my dad was in a car accident his chances of enjoying retirement pretty much disappeared. I told myself there are no guarantees, I should enjoy what I have now and so I did.

* * *

Tuesday. This afternoon I told a friend about my interest in intuition and she said the Science of Mind Center used to offer classes. I called and they still do – it was tonight, and I went.

I passed the Center building twice before I finally found the driveway. I parked and climbed a small flight of steps to a sort of run-down building with a very old carpet.

Robert (the teacher), a man named Andrew, and I were the only three there. Robert is about 5'10", brown hair, sort of average looking and he doesn't seem like a minister. But when he started to talk I recognized by the words he used, by the questions he asked, that he knows what he's talking about with intuition.

After a while he asked me about my experience and then asked me to do a reading for Andrew. It was amazing! I didn't even close my eyes, I was just looking at him, and I saw an image at his left temple. I started talking, as Robert had coached me to do.

"I see a bluish/green color…it feels like it represents money…and I see a brown-haired woman in a long white skirt and blouse…or maybe it's a dress…she's barefoot sometimes, she's comfortable in bare feet…and she's moving like a dancer." I didn't know where this was coming from, it was just what I saw and what I felt.

"Is she coming toward me or going away?" Andrew asked.

"I don't see her going toward you, she feels distant."

"Will she ever come back?" he asked. I didn't think so but my critical mind took over because I sensed that this question was important to Andrew and I didn't know for sure that what I felt was correct.

I turned to Robert, "I'm being mental. I'm concerned with what Andrew wants to have happen."

Robert reminded me not to judge what I saw but just pass information along and let Andrew decide what to do with it.

I told Andrew I didn't feel that she was coming back, that it felt like there was a conflict about money.

We all sat quiet for a minute.

"Sounds like Denise," Robert said to Andrew.

"Yeah. Well, the problem between us *was* about money. She wanted me to change careers so I'd earn more. We still have some energy connecting us but I'm relieved that she isn't coming back."

A few minutes later I visualized an engagement ring and Andrew said she'd gotten engaged to someone else. *Thank you, Universe, for this experience.* I saw that woman so clearly with my eyes open that I would recognize her if I saw her on the street.

Afterwards, Robert reminded me not to judge what I see, and to always choose words I feel, sense and hear rather than ones I think.

Robert did a health reading on me and mentioned something with my right breast so I told them about my cancer. Andrew had a good idea – he suggested I stop saying the "cancer is gone," and instead, say "I'm well now." I like the idea, it feels even more positive. I'm really happy that I've found this place to study and kind of amazed at how much I see. I wonder what it's for?

* * *

March, 1998

Sunday. This morning I went to church at the Science of Mind Center. There were just a handful of people but it was interesting. Afterward, Robert told everyone that I was learning to do readings and that I'd give them one if they wanted. I wasn't sure I was ready to practice outside of the class but a woman in her late 50s who I'd never seen before came over and asked me to read for her. We went to a quiet room and I asked to hold a piece of her jewelry so she handed me her watch.

I closed my eyes and talked as the pictures came.

"I see an airplane over water…I see a train…an outdoor marketplace, kind of a bazaar in what looks like a foreign country. I see you at the top of the subway escalator and someone just tried to pick your pocket but I don't get any sense of danger. I see, it's like I'm looking out from inside a car, I see a green countryside, open fields of tall grass, and then the car pulls up to a large home. There are no other houses nearby."

The airplane seemed obvious – if you leave Oahu you fly over water. The rest puzzled me because there aren't any transit trains on the island, no subways and I definitely wasn't seeing a local outdoor market.

I opened my eyes and the woman was looking at me, smiling.

"Do you want to know what that means to me?"

Of course, I did! Robert tells me that it doesn't matter if the subject can relate to what I'm seeing, that I'm seeing something that is true, but it still makes me feel better when they do.

"In two weeks I'm going to England, by plane," she said. "Last time I was there someone did attempt to pick my pocket at the tube station but it didn't make me afraid, just more careful. I'll be careful on this trip, too.

"I'll travel by train and I recognize the marketplace you saw, it's someplace I go when I'm in London. And I'll be taken by private car through the grassy green countryside to visit a friend in her large country home." She was beaming now.

I'm so thankful for this reading, I feel the information is being given to me to confirm that there are ways of knowing things beyond the five senses we all agree on. But what am I supposed to do with this information?

We went back into the main room and another woman asked for a reading. She looked obviously unwell but I still wasn't prepared for what happened. I closed my eyes and immediately saw a small river and a group of people on the other side, facing me, with their arms reaching out lovingly.

I felt this meant that she was going to "cross over" soon and that her support system was already there to help her but that wasn't something I wanted to say so I omitted the part about the river and just said that I saw a loving group of people reaching out to her to help. She didn't tell me what she thought that meant but she seemed happy to hear it.

* * *

Tuesday. This afternoon I got another letter from work. The owner says I'm being terminated at the end of March and I should look for other insurance.

I felt a momentary flash of alarm then let it go. Can she let me go while I'm on disability? I could easily let myself panic but I tell myself that I'll be okay.

I haven't been dancing in a while and I heard that Robert Cordoba, a hotshot dancer/teacher from the mainland, was going to be at Pecos teaching so I decided to go and get my mind off things I don't want to worry about.

* * *

Wednesday. I called TDI to ask if the owner can let me go while I'm on temporary disability and apparently she can. Progress, though… I didn't panic. In *Conversations With God,* the author says that being evolved doesn't mean challenging things won't keep happening. It means they will cease to cause us pain. I'm happy to notice that apart from a momentary flash of fear, I didn't feel too worried. But I do need insurance. I decided to call the State about insurance for the poor which, let's face it, I am. Then I'll call unemployment. I know I'm still not at the place where I can hold a regular job and not be stressed and stress = cancer. Sigh.

* * *

March 5. Thursday. Happy Birthday to Me. Today was fun. Art called at 7:30 a.m. from California to be the first one to wish me happy birthday. Tricia called and we decided I'll go visit her during the summer. I love that whenever I suggest visiting she's so happy.

Julie's in town so we met for lunch and caught up on each others' news and tonight Sid and I met for a sunset and dinner celebration. He sipped chardonnay. I sipped orange-flavored soda water. Dr. P said I could have a piece of birthday cake so we split the Chart House's incredible chocolate mud pie. Better, even, than Butterfingers. In four weeks we'll do the same thing to celebrate his birthday.

* * *

Tuesday. Tonight I went to the intuition class and Robert and I were the only ones there. He asked me if I'd do a reading for him and as I closed my eyes and started a body scan an image came immediately.

"I see a valentine in the position of your heart," I said. "That's a happy image, so I feel it means that your heart is good. I see a fall on an icy road that injured your right knee and I feel there was alcohol involved."

"I've had heart trouble in the past," Robert said, "and now I feel I'm in good shape so that's a good confirmation. I did fall on an icy road in Chicago one night and I injured my right knee. I don't remember alcohol being involved."

* * *

Wednesday. Between classes I practice intuition every time I think about it and the results are very interesting. At a bank of elevators I'll notice which car "feels" like it will be down next and go stand in front of it. Most of the time I'm right. Every time I come home I notice how many messages it "feels" like there are on my answering machine and then how many are from men and how many from women. I'm right so much of the time I'm surprised when I'm wrong. When I go someplace I ask *what unexpected thing will I see?* One time I "saw"someone fall on the dance floor and that night someone fell .

This morning I went to a meeting of writers and on the way, I tried to visualize what I'd find. I got a sense that the meeting room would be toward the left from the parking lot, that the doors would actually be on the side wall, that there'd be a platform on the front wall; I visualized how the seating would be arranged, how the leader

would be dressed and I was pleased, but not surprised,
that everything was exactly the way I'd seen it.

* * *

Thursday. This afternoon I did a reading for my
friend Karen in Kailua. Even though Robert tells me I
don't need this crutch, I feel like I do so I asked her to
bring a piece of jewelry or something with her energy on
it for me to hold during the reading. She handed me a
drop earring. I closed my eyes and watched as an image
developed, kind of like a picture in a pan of photo devel-
oping fluid.

"I see a motorcycle. I see a man with wire-rimmed
glasses. I see a couple in an old Model-T type car heading
away on a narrow dirt road."

Karen said her boyfriend gave her the earrings.
He rides a motorcycle and wears wire-rimmed glasses.

We pondered the significance of the car on the
dusty road. She and her boyfriend are having troubles
so we wondered if that meant they'll work things out
and grow old together? She asked if the road I saw was
smooth? Yes. Gentle curves, gentle slopes, nothing wild
or rugged.

* * *

Friday. Tonight I went to Rumours to dance and
when it got too loud and too crowded some friends and I
went to La Mariana to hear the singers.

During the day, La Mariana is a quiet place to
have lunch. A giant parrot squawks its welcome at the
door, wicker tables and chairs fill a closed-in patio and
next to that, a small dining room. Outside, a few dozen
small boats sway as the water laps lazily in the breeze.

But Friday and Saturday nights the place is
packed. When the Tahitian Lanai was torn down, the
blind pianist and the crowd who sang there moved to La

Mariana. They start around 9:30, two dozen or so regulars stand in front of the fish tank and sing a collection of old show tunes and Hawaiian songs. Tourists don't know about La Mariana, couldn't find it if they did, so it stays very local.

At 12:30 a.m. everyone stands, holds hands to sing *God Bless America*, then the *Hawaiian National Anthem* and finally, *Aloha Oi*. I sang the words I know, pretended some others and blinked away tears. Sometimes I feel very lonely here but at the same time it makes me feel like I belong in Hawaii. If I ever have to leave my heart will break.

* * *

Thursday. I've made it five months. I'm still seeing Dr. P every three or four weeks and still taking all the supplements he prescribes. Today his receptionist told me a stunner.

"He thinks you're doing very well." I asked how she knew.

"Because I asked him about both of us. He said that with the kind of cancer we had if we weren't doing well we'd both be dead now." Uhhhhhh!!! She said that the kind of cancer we had doubles in size every 60 days.

I'm still listening to the Caroline Myss tapes a lot and am still reminding myself to notice where my energy is. I know how to disassociate from stressful people and things and I tell myself I'll do it every night before I go to bed but I don't. Why is this so hard for me?

* * *

Saturday. I applied for unemployment and I'm pretty sure I'll get it since I've been let go. Money is *really* tight. I was barely surviving on my old salary and disability insurance pays even less. Organic food is *really* expensive.

I'm still going to qigong classes but I'm more and more frustrated that I can't do the moves in the right order and feel the energy move at the same time. I've decided to stop the class and just practice at home.

* * *

Monday. This afternoon I got a letter from the unemployment office saying I don't qualify since I'd quit. Quit? I didn't quit! I made myself take a few deep breaths before I called the number on the bottom of the letter.

"Your previous employer stated that you quit voluntarily," the counselor said. I told her the owner had written me a letter saying she was letting me go. The counselor asked if I could send her a copy. You bet I can!

* * *

April, 1998

Monday. Last month Greenwich U sent me a letter saying tuition is going up April 15. I definitely don't want to pay the new rate so I'm going to trust my gut and send my tuition $$$. I'm going to consider it an investment – an escape from having to spend the rest of my life working for crazy people.

* * *

Friday. I'm polishing up the picture book and sending queries out for a book about single parenting and fantasizing that it will make me a bunch of money.

I hate how so much of what I do is so money-driven, but it is. I started shopping for a computer. As usual, the cheapest one I can find. I don't really need a new computer except that I need to be able to use the Internet and my old computer is too old. After a bunch of phone calls I found a company that builds them to the customer's specifications so I only have to pay for what I absolutely need.

* * *

Tuesday. My new computer came (yea) with a new software program (ugh) to learn and I'm also struggling to figure out the Internet. I was determined to have it all mastered in a week. *Me, workaholic? Nah.* I bought one of the *Dummies* books and it helps some except when what the book shows doesn't match what I see on my screen.

Sometimes I wish I were living on some remote tropical island. But wait, I am! I mean I wish I lived on a remote tropical island without computers or Internet. Donne tells me not to push myself, not to stress, she says it'll get done when it gets done. Easy for her to say. She's already a whiz at both.

* * *

Wednesday. Dr. Silke did some muscle testing and I'm relieved that she says my body says there's no cancer and there's no need for cancer – meaning there's no psychological reason my body needs to create illness in order for me to…whatever. She encouraged me to set aside time to play and I remember someone else suggested I make an appointment with myself. Actually mark it on my calendar. Why/how do I keep myself so busy when I don't even have a job!

* * *

Thursday. April 16th. Today I celebrated the six-month anniversary of my cancer surgery. It's a BIG relief to be able to believe I'm not going to die. I think back six months ago, for awhile I was pretty sure I wouldn't survive the year. I feel very grateful to all the women who shared their cancer survival stories with me and helped me find my own way. I'm journaling so I can help other women someday.

I feel like I've made good progress. I have a new way of thinking about food and how essential *good food,* fresh, unprocessed, relatively free of chemicals, is and I'll never go back to frozen dinners.

I've made a commitment to never, Never, NEVER let myself get into – or at least stay in – another impossibly stressful job. I can walk away from crazy-making men pretty quickly – so I should be able to walk away from a crazy-making job.

I'm learning to notice when my thinking is negative or judgmental and to pull my attention back and put it on something positive. Why is all this so hard?

* * *

Friday. I got a letter from the unemployment folks granting me unemployment for six months. It's a BIG relief.

* * *

Monday. Today I had my first phone conversation with my first mentor at Greenwich. The University is willing to give me college credit for some of the work I've already done, like the books I've written, the dozens of workshops and seminars I've taken and I might get credit for teaching at UH. But I have to document everything I've done very carefully and outline my course curricula and make it into a work project report.

The notion of taking on such a large project at this time feels overwhelming but at the same time I feel like this is what I have to do now in order to do what I want to do later.

* * *

Thursday. Aaaaarrrrgh! I think noisy neighbors who don't work should all live in the same building and quiet people who work at home should live with other quiet people. It's always warm so of course my windows and doors are always open and so are theirs and most of the time I could tape record their conversations from my living room, they are that loud. I wish I could be one of those cheery people who could go over there, make a joke and get them to be half as considerate a neighbor as I am. But I'm not and so I can't.

Instead, I try to rise above it all. Not too successfully. If I stop focusing on what I don't like it won't bother me so much, right? Well, that's the theory.

I hear the gate clang whenever anyone comes or goes; I hear one neighbor's sandals slap-slap up the stairs. There is someone in the building beside ours who moans loudly, painfully, every hour or so and that disturbs me. The landlord says there's a nurse over there who gives the man pain medication and that explains the quiet times. It bothers me that he has to hurt. There is a woman in the building in front who screams ugly things at her young children. A neighbor and I holler at her that we're going to call the cops and she is quiet. For the millionth time I wish I could tune out noise. Or afford to move.

I've always liked being alone but more and more I find myself feeling lonely. I remind myself that being alone gives me freedom and it gives me options. I feel blessed to be able to live in Hawaii. I feel blessed to have teachers to teach me how to meditate, to teach me how to develop my intuition, blessed that Dad has offered to take care of my medical bills, blessed to be well. I feel blessed to be starting work on my bachelor's so I'll have a degree. Blessed to have Tricia. I just wish I had a best friend who has time to talk, time to go to lunch, time to go to a movie now and then or even casual friends to go laugh and play with. Everyone here is so busy! And Mr. Wonderful. That would be nice.

* * *

Sunday. I've surprised myself by making time to meditate every day for a week – 20 minutes in the morning and 20 minutes in the evening. After a few minutes my body gets hot and sometimes I realize I'm not aware of whether I'm breathing or not. I've started sleeping better.

* * *

Tuesday. It's rained for nearly two weeks. I'm desperate to find sun so I called the concierge at the Turtle Bay Hilton but he said it was gray there too, so I stayed home, again, and sent out queries. I sent out resumes to Goodwill (not sure I could teach handicapped people, though, not sure I could connect with them) and to Big Brothers/ Big Sisters (since I was a big sister for four years I know I'd like working there). I've called every single non-profit agency in the phone book asking about job openings and I've sent out dozens of resumes they promise to hold "in case something opens up."

I make sure to notice how I "feel" when I'm preparing each cover letter and a couple of times I've thrown ads away because I notice the muscles in my belly tighten when I read them.

* * *

Wednesday. A lady from Greenwich called, asking me to choose a program mentor. I chose a woman who has her Ph.D. in psychology and who works in the business community as an intuitive. I'm excited, ready to go.

* * *

Late May, 1998

Monday. I still feel like I'm scrambling a lot, like I'm on a treadmill with a carrot out there someplace that I never seem to reach. I'm sending out queries for books I'd buy if I were an editor (especially *The Single Parent*

Survival Guide), and getting back friendly not-quite-right-but-try-again letters. Every writer knows stories about famous books that were rejected 20 times before finding a home so I'm trying to be philosophical.

* * *

Saturday. I was cleaning out drawers and found an old manuscript I'd always thought had promise. A collection of practices I came up with years ago that I think could change a person's life. They worked for me – why did I stop? Why do I do that? I find something really helpful and then I get lazy or distracted, I forget about it and slide back into my old ways. Okay, I'm still learning. Good time to start them again. I printed out a copy for my bedroom and another one for the kitchen.

> 10 Practices That Will Bring You Peace,
> Happiness and Success
> 1. *Let Go of Attachments to Outcomes*
> 2. *Notice the Behavior Patterns You Slip Into*
> 3. *Listen to the Stories You Tell Yourself*
> 4. *Let Go of Ego-based Addictions*
> 5. *Let Go of Judgments*
> 6. *Take Care of Yourself First*
> 7. *Think, Talk About and Notice the Positive*
> 8. *Accept 100 Percent Responsibility for Everything*
>   *in Your Life*
> 9. *Trust Yourself*
> 10. *Trust the Universe.*

I grabbed a notebook, went to the Surfrider and camped out on the porch to think about these practices.

1. *Let Go of Attachments to Outcomes*. I discovered this one night after I'd learned hypnosis. I'd gone to consult with someone who'd been a hypnotherapist for years and he'd put me in a trance that left me more relaxed,

more confident and peaceful than I had ever been in my life. Afterwards, he'd asked me what I'd need to change in my life to feel like that all the time and I'd known the answer without having to think even for a second: I'd have to let go of my attachments to the way things turned out.

As kids, we were taught just the opposite. We're taught that if we want something we have to work hard, we have to go after it relentlessly, we have to keep after it until we make it happen.

I know I created the writing job at the Auto Club with sheer energy but it turned out to be a very stressful job. Maybe if I hadn't pushed so hard, I'd have found one that would have been kinder to me. When I'm so locked into having one thing I have blinders on and I don't notice, or I'm not willing to explore other, maybe better possibilities. When I'm attached to getting one thing it's too easy to disregard negative information that I really should pay attention to.

The day after the hypnosis session I put a Post-it note on my credenza at work asking, *Attached?* I was selling wine on the phone, commission only, and it was scary. But I taught myself to notice when I was feeling angry, frustrated, afraid, etc. and to stop and think about what I was attached to. It would be something like having the customer buy, having him give me a chance, not hang up on me...and when I recognized what I was attached to, I would choose to let it go and hold what I wanted to have happen as a goal, instead. Then I could dial the next number without dragging energy from the last one along.

It was amazing the difference it made. I became relaxed and confident and I started selling more wine and winning a lot of the sales contests. I even became good phone friends with dozens of my customers.

I handled moving to Hawaii with this practice. I let go of my attachments to having a job before I went, let go of my attachment to having the perfect place to live. I let go of my attachment to knowing exactly how things would turn out and held what I wanted as a goal.

If I'd rememered about attachments when I was waiting to be interviewed for this last sales job I'd have walked out before the interview, or at the very least, I'd have quit that first day when my body was screaming for me to escape. I'd had valid reasons to leave at least once a week after that but I was attached to proving I could be calm in a company of difficult people, attached to staying till Christmas so I could make money.

But I remembered the practice when I needed to let go of my attachment to surviving this cancer (though I really hope I will). Not being attached gave me the courage to explore other ways to be well.

2. *Notice the Behavior Patterns You Slip Into.* I still want to fix everything and everyone and that's a hard habit to say no to. I used to believe that if there was anything at all that I could possibly do to help someone I was morally required to do it, whether they'd asked or not, and that I was a bad person if I didn't. I don't believe that anymore but I still feel powerful urges to make things better. That was another thing that kept me at this job too long. I knew I could fix what wasn't working there.... I forgot that *that* wasn't my job.

Another behavior pattern I slip into is victim mode. When I first started selling wine I had a terrible time. I blamed my lack of sales on the high cost of the wine, the bad economy, the leads, the training...turned out my low sales didn't have anything to do with that. Once I started letting go of my attachments to outcomes and started having fun with the job I stopped being a victim and started selling as much, often more, than the others.

Now I'm refusing to be a victim and am determined to take care of myself.

I have a life-long habit of standing up to authority for awhile and then giving in and doing it their way. But I have not given in, I will not give in, to the doctors who tell me their way is the only way.

Workaholic? Hi, my name is Karin.... Well, I was definitely not a workaholic when I was in school, despite teacher and parental urgings, but over the years I've connected overworking with being responsible, dedicated, valuable and getting applause so now I have a hard time knowing when to stop. Even when no one is watching, I'm a workaholic. But I need to learn to balance work with play for my health and my sanity.

3. *Let Go of the Stories You Tell Yourself*. Stories like I'm not good enough, I don't have the skills/looks/education (fill in the blanks) to (fill in the blank). Stories that I have to be nice all the time, and successful, and perfect.... These stories are strongly imbedded because they're the stories I grew up hearing and they keep getting reinforced at jobs and in just about all the magazines I read.

One of the wonderful benefits from the weekly Arnold Patent support group I went to for years was that the other members told me wonderful things they saw in me and I could start replacing my old stories with these new, better ones. Now it's up to me to do it for myself.

I'm trying to let go of the story that says I have to work hard to figure out how to be well instead of just spending time relaxing and writing.

4. *Let Go of Ego-based Addictions.* Ah, yes. Those things that make my ego shout at me when it thinks I'm not being perfect, right, the best, in control; getting praise, attention, everything (I think) I deserve. I've still got some addictions but now I think I notice when they pop up and sometimes I can decide to detach, I can just let them go.

5. *Let Go of Judgments.* This one confused me for a while, because I believed it meant I had to be positive about everything. I spent an uncomfortable three years with a roommate because when we met I *thought* I was being judgmental. Too late, I realized that the way my body felt was my intuition telling me that we weren't a good match.

My logical mind told me I was being judgmental when I wasn't comfortable at that sales job while my *feelings* screamed at me to escape.

6. *Take Care of Yourself First.* Clearly, I need help with this one but I'm getting better. At least it's on my mind. I need to stop making more projects for myself; I need to go to the beach at least once a week; I need to stop working at a certain time; I need to take two days off on weekends; I need to go to the massage school at least once a month; meditate.... I don't have a job right now, how hard can all this be?????

I think that communicating honestly, even (or especially) to myself is a big part of this one. How many years did I spend stuffing what I longed to say because speaking my feelings might hurt someone else's feelings or might make them think of me in a less favorable way? I didn't speak up when I should have at this last sales job but think I do now. More, anyway.

7. *Think, Talk About and Notice the Positive.* Thank you, Caroline Myss. I'm pretty aware of this. I don't watch

the news on TV, don't read the daily paper. I try to see the good in people and situations.

I believe that if I expect bad things to happen they will and if I expect good things to happen *they* will.

8. *Accept 100 Percent Responsibility for Everything in Your Life.* An old Religious Science lesson. I can and I do. Okay, first I react like a normal human being and fuss some but then I stop. I do really believe that I create everything. Some people would argue that I didn't create cancer (but maybe I did so I'd have this time to think) but I definitely created a body where it could flourish by always being stressed, by not doing things I needed to do to take care of myself (like relaxing, eating well, exercising).

9. *Trust Yourself.* Boy. This is important. In the past, when I've trusted myself it's been when others agreed. Choosing what I want to do and what I don't want to do for my cancer care is the first time I trusted myself against strong and ongoing opposition. Yea for me.

10. *Trust the Universe.* Yes. It's brought me everything (except Mr. Wonderful) I've every really wanted. From little things like buying a blouse with a unique button missing and finding the perfect match in my sewing box, to big things like finding a book on co-parenting at eye level in the library the day after my (soon-to-be ex) told me he didn't think co-parenting would work. I taught these practices for awhile in California. (For *10 Practices* workshop and book information see www.IrelandComm unications.com)

When I decided to move to Hawaii I had no idea how I could pull it off with no job, no friends there, no permanent place to live. But I knew it would all work out and one day a friend told me that her friend's friend rented rooms and I could stay there as long as I wanted to. Years later I told everybody I wanted an apartment with two bedrooms and an ocean view for the same rent I was paying for my one bedroom and everybody thought I was nuts but one day a friend called to say she'd found my ocean-view apartment while looking for one for herself. And the Universe led me to more than a dozen women on Oahu who could talk to me about ways they'd discovered to be well from cancer.

* * *

Sunday. A day doing nothing...kinda stressful!

* * *

June, 1998

Tuesday. I'm getting better at stopping to play. Several times a week I take a manuscript or a book and sit in the shade at Bellows, Lanakai, Sunset Beach, Turtle Bay.... When I go to Haleiwa I take the time to walk from one end of town to the other and back. At least once a week I claim a chair at one of the bookstores and read magazines and self-help books that catch my eye.

I still find myself taking on too many projects and so sometimes I still feel overwhelmed. I need to look at practices 3 and 4. What stories am I telling myself? What addictions am I giving in to? But I'm not feeling like I have to get everything done every day and this is progress. Why is it so hard to just slow down and have fun? All those old childhood tapes drive me but I'm trying to record over them with new messages.

* * *

Sunday. Went back to the Science of Mind Church after not going for a month or so and nothing has changed. After the service two people were reading palms and they offered to read mine. They pointed out that there are rings around my wrists and they said that indicates a long life. I finally feel like I will survive but still, whenever I hear it from someone else I take a moment to let the feeling of peace and happiness wrap around me.

* * *

July, 1998

Monday. Sid and I went to dance buddy Don's for the 4th of July. Don's beachfront condo is a wonderful place to watch fireworks from the show at Magic Island and it's nice to be here with people I usually only see dancing. I wish we'd all get together more often, I really would love to be part of a large, fun group but everyone here is just so busy. They say they want to do things but never seem to find (make) time to actually do it. (It kinda reminds me of me!)

I took the long weekend off – three days without working on anything!!! (Yea, I'm taking time for myself.)

* * *

August, 1998

Thursday. Finished my new picture book – *Don't Take Your Snake for a Stroll* – and sent it to an editor at Harcourt I've sent things to before. Cross fingers.

I'm still watching the paper for a job I might like. I miss helping other people so I'm sticking to social services type jobs.

Went to Pecos tonight; the dance crowd keeps shrinking so sometimes I only dance once or twice the whole night. When that happens I get frustrated and depressed and miss dancing in California. I think I miss it like a track star would miss running or a skier would miss the snow.

* * *

Tuesday. Another lonely day. There are beautiful beaches I could go to but I'm just not motivated. When I think about times I've felt joy I realize it's always been with people.

And where is Mr. Wonderful? Julie tells me that I'm too picky but I know that I'm not. True, my list of qualities I want in a partner is long but I'd rather be alone, lonely even, than with the wrong man.

I think back about the guys I've gone out with. Could there have been hope for the guy who invited me out to "split a muffin"? Or the one who professed his love but had to be in bed every night by 10 (alone)?

What about the men who were controlling or angry, or men who loved their car/boat/mother/dog/freedom more than they could ever love me? Might they have changed? Only in the movies, I think.

* * *

Friday. Yippee! Got a message on my machine from the editor I sent the *Snake* manuscript to saying she thinks this book might be the one! I called her to ask what that means and she says she likes the story a lot and will pitch it at next week's story conference. I asked her if she always gets to buy the books she wants and she laughed and said not always. But I know she's a senior editor there so I'm feeling pretty optimistic.

* * *

Thursday. The Harcourt editor called and she's buying my picture book! I'm floating. I'm so excited! Fun to know that she'll be sending me a little money in a couple of months, too. (*Don't Take Your Snake For a Stroll* was published by Harcourt in 2003.)

* * *

September, 1998

Friday. I've started a bunch of other picture books and am spending most of my time working on them. I wonder if this is what I'm meant to do. I think if I could sell enough of them, I could eventually have a peaceful life staying home writing. But I've been a full-time writer before, and eventually I miss people so much that I go out and get a regular job. Is everyone as confused about their path as I am? Or are most people not aware that there are choices?

I'm still taking Dr. P's pills and potions faithfully. I only eat organic fruits and vegetables. I eschew dairy, wheat, caffeine and sugar. I buy only non-toxic cosmetics and cleaning products. I feel like I should do these things for another year or so, and then I can move back to a more normal life.

I never have quite gotten with the exercise program but I keep promising that the next week I will. Does that count?

* * *

October, 1998

October 16. Friday. HAPPY ANNIVERSARY TO ME! One year! I'm alive! My latest mammogram showed no sign of cancer anywhere. I feel relieved, grateful, optimistic, the world is good and I'm going to survive!

You always hear people say that their cancer or heart attack or their near-fatal-accident was a blessing in disguise, something that woke them up to a greater awareness of life and I would sure say I feel that's true for me, too. I would never want to go through this year again, would never want anyone else to, but I also wouldn't erase the experience and go back to my old life.

I know my diet has changed forever. I'm finally honoring my life-long promise to myself to eat better. I have a good understanding of what kind of workplace I can be healthy in and I'm never going to take another job that causes me so much stress.

I'm paying attention to my body for signals that I am or am not moving in the right direction. I'm no longer willing to beat myself up if I don't conform to someone else's idea of who and what I should be.

I've claimed Sunday as a day I don't work, don't make any plans at all. I get up and do whatever I feel like doing. It's about time!

* * *

Thursday. I applied for a job with Lanakila Meals on Wheels and today Wendell called, said he liked my resume. The job would be working part time (but I'd have health insurance) at an elderly apartment building where lunches are served every weekday. I'd be responsible for recruiting and supervising volunteers and I'd be expected to present programs on safety, health and nutrition; I'd also be in charge of putting together entertainment programs, and plan recreational activities like bingo and bus trips to local attractions.

Would I be interested? Yes! It makes me happy to think about it – I've got an appointment to meet him next week.

* * *

Monday. Today was my interview with Wendell and Connie at Lanakila. They told me more about the job and asked how I was at conflict resolution.

With seniors? I asked what kinds of conflict there might be.

"Oh, sometimes two women get their eyes on the same man and they can get pretty angry. Or someone won't like the way someone talked to them or their friend...one woman chased a man with her cane."

"Wow, how old are these people?"

"Mostly 70s and 80s."

I told them what I'd do and I think I really want this job. I test it mentally against my belief that work = stress and then I notice how I feel. I feel that this job is low key enough that there won't be much stress – at least not the kind of stress I had at my old job. Yup, I really want this job.

* * *

Friday. Some people say there's discrimination in Hawaii, that the locals don't like the haoles and won't hire us but that's never been true for me and today Wendell called to offer me the job! I said yes. It feels good. I delayed my start date for two weeks so I can wrap up some projects and have some free time, too.

When I hung up I considered for about five seconds the idea of just walking away from all my projects and going someplace to play for two weeks – or even one – but I still have workaholic tendencies and a shrinking bank account. I need to figure out which projects to stop working on and which I should try to finish before I start work and which I want to work on in the afternoons when I come home. Would it be good discipline to just go play and get back to them whenever? Yup. But I can't. At least it's progress that I'm going to put some projects away instead of (old way) planning to keep working on everything and just adding the job on top.

* * *

December, 1998.

Tuesday. I love this job! The meal site is a huge recreation room on the fifth floor of Pohulani, a beautiful low-income elderly apartment building. One wall is windows and sliding glass doors; just outside there's a terrace with plants and a pool and most of the time, blue sky. It feels like a healthy place to be.

The food is all prepared at the Lanakila kitchen (mostly by workers who have physical or mental challenges) and delivered by van every day, then my group of 15 volunteers serve to the 40 to 60 other seniors who come for a hot meal.

What I love most about the job is the people. Such characters! Such big hearts. So willing to help each other and me and in a short time we – the volunteers, the diners and I – have become ohana, we're family.

I feel a calm happiness about this job, this location, these people. I can do good here, for them and for myself. Afternoons I'll finish working on my degree and see then what I feel like doing with it. I'll work on some of the writing projects I think have a good chance of paying off and I'll remember to play.

I know this job won't be right forever, but I trust that when it isn't, I'll know and I'll leave. Right now, though, I feel great, hopeful, optimistic.

I've come through, at times fought my way through, a terrifying experience. I've trusted myself to make brave decisions; I've kept an open mind, learned important lessons and I've survived.

I wish I thought I'd remember those lessons every day from now on but I know sometimes I'm going to forget. I'm not going to expect myself to be perfect anymore,

I'm going to give myself permission to be human and remember that I'm still learning.

* * *

Afterword

I stayed with the Meals-on-Wheels program for two years, happy to be working at a job where I helped people, happy to be with friends every day. Then management changed their focus. They wanted us to spend less time with the seniors and instead work part-time in the office. We were given multiple sites to supervise so that we'd only be at some sites once or twice a week, and more and more of the day-to-day work and responsibility for running the program was to be left to the seniors.

We tried to explain to management that these people, in their 70s, 80s and 90s, didn't want the responsibility of record keeping or of supervising their peers, but management made the changes anyway. Several group leaders quit and I'm happy to say I was one of them.

Saying goodbye to those seniors who had filled me up with love was one of the hardest things I've ever done, but the job was becoming stressful, I needed more money, and I knew it was time to leave.

I took a full-time job recruiting foster and adoptive families for children in the custody of the State. I loved it and felt good to have another job doing something that mattered. My favorite part was the pre-parent training and I remembered how much I enjoy coaching.

By the time my inner voice started nudging me to leave Hawaii, I was ready. I could look back and see events that had begun to shake me loose: Pecos had closed but on visits to the mainland I could dance the two-step and west-coast swing all night. I remembered walking through a crisp fall Sacramento morning with Tricia, kicking up red and orange and yellow leaves and thinking *this could be fun*.... I remembered when she and I had gone to Manhattan together and it had been such an adventure, so much fun not to know what was around every corner.

I still loved Hawaii but after six years I knew what was around every corner. I knew every beach, every rock, every restaurant, every shop, nothing was new anymore. I missed having adventures. And since Mr. Wonderful still hadn't shown up, I decided to go have adventures by myself.

I thought about moving to California, where the weather was good and I'd be close to Tricia, but it felt like going back and I wanted to move forward. I remembered that years before I'd seen TV coverage of a flood in Austin, Texas, and for some reason I'd been fascinated by the tall, thin trees clustered on the river bank. The city's website showed a picturesque bridge, a river that meandered through the town and I felt curious. I figured a college town meant open-minded people and Texas meant country music and two-step dancing. I started asking around and everyone who'd been to Austin raved about the town.

I saved my money, didn't buy anything I wouldn't take with me, and a year later, on November 11, 2001, I stepped off the plane in my new home.

I got a job with the American Cancer Society in Austin, answering calls from people who wanted to quit smoking. I liked the job, liked that I could be helping people, but two months later my entire team was told we needed to retrain, we were being moved to the cancer information call lines and would be giving out information to people who called with questions.

I looked at the data base, and the Cancer Society was passing along the same information I'd fought so hard to get past. I knew that as an employee I'd only be allowed to give callers the standard information and I wouldn't be able to talk about my experience or any of the wonderful doctors I'd read about.

I explained my conflict to my supervisor and asked her to let me stay in the stop smoking program. She said no and gave me till the end of the week to leave.

As I walked out the door for the last time, I was encouraged that I'd spent less time and energy trying to "fix" my employer than ever before. I realized that it was time to start writing this book.

A few months later I was standing at the cookie table at an Austin Writer's League meeting and my soul mate walked over and introduced himself. Of course I didn't know he was my soul mate right away, but Francis was interesting, and charming, and sweet, and funny. In the next few months I realized he had every quality I'd wanted in a man plus some I'd only dreamed of; after being single for 20 years, Mr. Wonderful had finally found me! I realized it hadn't been the trees that had drawn me to Austin, it had been *him*.

October 16, 2002, was the five-year anniversary of my cancer surgery and I felt a sense of jubilation and relief; I'd done it my way, I'd survived. I had learned valuable lessons, I'd found Mr. Wonderful and life was good. I sent e-mails out to my family and friends sharing the good news and thanking them for their support. Everyone sent happy e-mails back.

Three weeks later I went for a routine mammogram and a few days later got a letter saying no abnormalities had been found. After every mammogram I waited anxiously for the report and I was happy and relieved that this one held good news. But the following week a clerk called to ask to see previous X-rays.

I hung up the phone and thought, *no problem.* Okay, a little problem. I couldn't help but worry. Why did they want to see them? I took the old X-rays from Hawaii in that afternoon.

"The doctor would like to do a magnification mammogram on your left breast," the clerk said. *Left? My other breast?* I told myself they were just being overly cautious, since I had a history of cancer.

I waited for the technician to come back and say I could leave. Instead, she came back with a man in a white lab coat and the minute I saw him I felt that too-familiar feeling of dread.

"This is Dr. McClurg," she said. He put my X-rays up on a light box and showed me this year's and last year's views.

"There's a shadow here. Generally a shadow this dark indicates a cancer. You should have a needle biopsy to see what it is, perhaps a surgical biopsy."

Fear that I'd never expected to feel again gripped me, also despair, disbelief, and confusion, frustration, anger.... How could this be happening, *again?* Hadn't I done everything I was supposed to do? I knew my diet had slipped some but still, I knew it was better than the next 100 people who'd come through the door and *not* have cancer. I felt betrayed. I went home and told Francis, and sobbed.

I hated having fear be part of my life again. I'd just met my soul mate and it didn't seem fair that I might die so soon but, of course, I knew that life isn't fair. I tried to be positive. Maybe the doctor was wrong.

Tricia came to visit with her new baby, Ireland, and when I told her we all cried again. Later, we tried to be normal and have fun, but always in the back of our minds was the question, *what if...?* A few days later we went to see the surgeon my OB/GYN had recommended.

"This shadow here," she said pointing, "is very dark. It looks like cancer." I looked at the X-ray, saw the spidery roots and my eyes filled with tears. I didn't want to be going through this again. Francis looked sad. Tricia put a comforting arm around my shoulder. I rocked my new granddaughter on my lap, this precious new baby I wanted to have fun with and love. If I died from this she wouldn't even remember me.

In the week before the surgery, Francis and I practiced thinking and talking about what we wanted, pushing aside thoughts of what we didn't want. We cried and told ourselves it was okay to cry, even if we knew everything would be fine. We bought a journal and made a list of all the places we planned to visit and the things we planned to do during the next 20 years we're married and vowed we'd do it all. I asked friends to visualize me dancing at Irie's wedding. Francis and I reminded each other that the surgeon could be wrong.

It was a bad time but, I realized, not as bad as the first time. This time I was less confused about what to do, more optimistic that I would survive.

I struggled not to blame myself for having cancer again – maybe I should have kept taking Dr. P's potions. Maybe I should have stayed on my absolutely-no-sugar diet. Maybe moving, starting new jobs, living an unstructured life was more stress than my body could cope with. Maybe if I'd started exercising....

Then I'd remind myself that second guessing is always a waste of energy and that I deserved to feel proud of the changes I *had* made. I told myself to stop asking *what if* and instead ask myself *what now?*

On November 25, 2002, I had a 1.5 cm invasive ductal carcinoma removed from my left breast.

"The good news," my surgeon said, "is that I got clean margins. And it was a different kind of cancer so we know it didn't spread from the previous cancer.

"I recommend you have radiation therapy," she paused and waited for my response. I shook my head. It didn't feel right for me.

"Well, you seemed to have had good success with your treatment plan last time, so do what you did then again."

I called Sherry and she did another intuitive reading for me. She said my breasts looked clean of cancer. That I needed to rely on myself in a good way and not get lost in such a strong desire to succeed. She said to remember that I'm very strong and my strength comes from a spiritual place, I need to trust it and surrender to that trust. She said that what's happening now is a real leap for me, almost a meltdown to get to what is essential, to get to my heart. She repeated something she'd said last time – I've always used so much of my masculine energy to make things happen and it's time to shift to more feminine energy. She said I needed to trust myself.

Everything she said felt true. A couple of days later I noticed the fear I'd attached to having cancer sort of slip away. I was grateful that I didn't have to repeat the chaos of my first cancer diagnosis and I was interested to notice that within weeks I seemed to be able to put the event behind me as if I'd had my appendix out. Except that you can only have your appendix out once and now I'll never be able to think I know for sure that I won't have cancer again.

The following spring I got a job, partly for the money but mostly so I'd have health insurance since my

COBRA was running out. At first I was enthusiastic, because I was helping people who wanted to adopt and I went home every day feeling good.

Then my job was restructured and it became the worst job of my life! I tried every positive-thinking technique I knew and made up a few new ones but nothing helped. I dreaded going to work, was miserable while I was there, and dragged myself home every evening to recover. Francis urged me to quit but I told him and myself that I couldn't. Tricia said that the irony was that I was holding on to the job so I'd have insurance and the job was so stressful that it was pretty much going to guarantee that I'd need it. She said it sadly, not as a joke.

I knew she was right, could even see that staying went against everything I believed about the importance of taking care of myself. But the voice that warned that since I'd had cancer, *twice* I'd never be able to get insurance, spoke louder and I told myself I had to stay at least till I could get COBRA again. I marked off the days on my calendar till I could escape.

The only bright spot during this time was that on June 21, after I'd been single for 20 years, Francis and I were married in a beautiful Hawaiian ceremony in wilderness behind his son's Texas Hill Country home. Family flew in from around the country. A Hawaiian Kahu I'd met in San Antonio drove up to perform a traditional ceremony complete with drums and chants and sacred blessings.

I'd told Francis I'd always thought I'd be married on the beach in Hawaii, so, as a surprise, he had bags of sand brought in to make a beach for us to stand on. One of his daughter's surprised me by air-shipping us white ginger leis from Honolulu and it was one of the happiest days of my life.

I went back to work a few days later. While I'd been gone, my job had been further restructured so that computer data entries and impossible deadlines would fill my day. It didn't help that I wasn't the only one stressed, that the whole office was charged with angry energy. I went home that evening and never went back. My inner voice had been sending me messages to leave for months but I'd listened to the wrong voices.

As I finish this book a year later, I realize I've spent most of my life listening to the wrong voices. I listened to parents and teachers who told me I had to work hard to succeed and that only certain traditional behaviors could be labeled success. I listened when they told me it was selfish to consider myself first, that I should never put my wants or needs in front of somebody else's. I listened to employers who hired me because of who I am and then asked me to change, I listened to men who wanted me to be who they thought I should be and I listened to our culture, which says truly valuable women are complacent but hard working and they all multi-task.

When I think back, I recognize that those voices caused me most of the pain and confusion I've had in my life. Those, and the voice of my ego. The voice of my ego speaks loudest when it's afraid I won't get one of the things I'm attached or addicted to and I used to confuse it with my inner voice. But the voice of my ego doesn't care about me, it cares about the messages parents, teachers, employers, etc. programmed me with.

My inner voice speaks softly, patiently, but per-sistently. It suggests and nudges me in the right direction. It only becomes intense when I don't listen and the stakes are high. This voice cares nothing about my ego; its goal is always to take care of me.

Finally, I have the voices sorted out and I know which one to listen to. It helps that I've stopped putting myself in impossible situations. It helps that (most of the time) I've stopped expecting myself to be perfect. Making changes requires practice. I'm remembering to have balance between work and play, to exercise (finally) and to laugh. Most of all, I'm remembering to trust myself.

Some Final Thoughts

In the years since my first cancer diagnosis, some things have changed. The medical community was stunned to learn that nearly half of all U.S. adults use some form of alternative medicine. Imagine how they felt when they learned their patients spent an estimated $30 billion on alternative care. After dismissing it as quackery for decades, economics demanded that the traditional medical machine shift gears.

To realign themselves with those same alternative practices they'd been so quick to shun the medical establishment created a new label, Complementary and Alternative Medicine (CAM), and vowed to evaluate the therapies so many people already trust. They talk of blended or integrative medicine. They want their part of that $30 billion.

The December 2, 2002 issue of *Newsweek* devoted 31 pages to exploring forms of alternative medicine including acupuncture, music therapy and traditional Chinese medicine. Selenium, glucosamine and chondroitin sulfate, and ginkgo biloba are just a few of the supplements under examination. The downside is that writers of these articles, mostly doctors, see some therapies as only contributing a minor role to wellness. But it's a start.

Many U.S. universities (including Harvard and Duke) are exploring and even teaching alternative therapies. But the fact that they're exploring doesn't mean they will accept them as wholeheartedly as their patients have. Change happens slowly with medicine.

You may have heard about Ignaz Philipp Sem-
melweis. He was a Hungarian doctor born in 1818 who
died insane because the scientific world refused to accept
his simple solution to a medical problem that was killing
thousands of women every year. The medical problem
was puerperal infection, or childbed fever. His solution
was for doctors to wash their hands between patients.

Even when scientific studies do point the way
for change, information takes a while to trickle down.
Individual doctors may be reluctant to be the first ones to
change, even after they believe it may be a good thing.

A 2002 issue of *AARP Bulletin* noted that a study
had proven that radiation after a lumpectomy with clean
margins resulted in the same outcome as a lumpectomy
without radiation. But one month later my surgeon had
recommended radiation to me.

And the January 2003 issue of the same *Bulletin*
ran this headline: "Scam Alert, Cancer and Snake Oil."
Some of the treatments they scorn as snake-oil cures are
ones reputable M.D.s around the country have found *do*
help in certain aspects of cancer care.

I believe that there is no absolute one way to treat
cancer. It makes sense that a good diet is the fuel that drives
our bodies yet doctors traditionally get little information
on nutrition so they don't give it as much attention as
they should. It makes sense to boost our immune system,
whether we use traditional therapies or not, but most doctors haven't been taught about that and they only know
the medicine learned in medical school, passed along in
medical journals, or supplied by drug companies.

Understandably, the drug companies resist therapies they can't patent and sell and drug companies fund
buildings and fellowships at medical schools. Of course
they pass along information that benefits them and most

physicians are reluctant to stray far from protocols they're taught or from protocols their peers use.

Since the turn of the century there have been dozens of physicians who have treated cancer patients very successfully with non-traditional therapies.

Do they always work? No.

Does radiation or chemotherapy? No.

There are many ways to solve most problems and that's true with cancer, too. Doctors in Goldberg's book have a variety of potential protocols to consider and hopefully, in the near future, *every* physician will have; I think then the survival rate will improve.

Until that happens, we need to keep learning, we need to take responsibility for deciding what's best for ourselves, ourselves. We need to learn to trust ourselves.

Karin Ireland

July 2004

Resources

Burton Goldberg Presents an Alternative Medicine Definitive Guide to Cancer, edited by Burton Goldberg, Future Medicine Publishing

Cancer Diagnosis: What to Do Next, W. John Diamond, M.D. and W. Lee Cowden, M.D. with Burton Goldberg, Alternative Medicine.com Books

Positive Energy, Judith Orloff, M.D., Harmony Books

The Complete Natural Medicine Guide to Breast Cancer, Sat Dharam Kaur, ND, Robert Rose Inc.

Love, Medicine and Miracles, Bernie Siegel M.D., Perennial

Life Without Limits, Robert B. Stone, Ph.D., Llewyllen Publications

Since Strangling Isn't an Option, Sandra Crowe M.A., A Perigee Book

10 Practices That Will Bring You Peace, Confidence and Success, Karin Ireland. For workshop and book information see www.IrelandCommunications.com

Optimum Health Institute
San Diego. CA: 619 464-3346
Austin, TX: 512 303-4817

Sherry Vinson, Intuitive, e-mail sgv@rockisland.com

These resources are offered as an option to explore with no guarantees of result.

Books By Karin Ireland

Self-Help
10 Practices That Will Bring You Peace, Confidence and
   Success
Boost Your Child's Self-Esteem
150 Ways to Help Your Child Succeed
How to Have All the Answers When the Questions
   Keep Changing
The Best Christmas Ever: How to Recapture the True
   Spirit of the Holidays
The Job Survival Instruction Book

Humor
Boyfriends Live Longer Than Husbands Because...
It's Not a Lie If...
How to Cheat On Your Budget

Children's Books
The Secret Life of Piggies
Don't Take Your Snake For A Stroll
Would You Still Love Me...?
Mama's Helper
My Mom and Dad Are Just Friends
Wonderful Nature, Wonderful You
Albert Einstein
Helicopters at Work
Kitty O'Neil, Daredevil Woman
Hollywood Stuntpeople

Audio Tapes
Guided Imagery: Wellness Before and After Surgery/
   Reducing Pain
Guided Imagery: Messages of Wellness During Your
   Surgery